Failure to Thrive in Young Children

RESEARCH AND PRACTICE EVALUATED

Failure to Thrive in Young Children

RESEARCH AND PRACTICE EVALUATED

Jane A. Batchelor

UNIVERSITY OF BATH

A Voluntary Society of The Church of England and The Church in Wales

First published in 1999

The Children's Society
Edward Rudolf House
Margery Street
London WC1X 0JL

A catalogue record of this book is available from the British Library.

ISBN 1 899783 25 3

Typeset and designed by Bookcraft Ltd, Stroud

CONTENTS

Foreword   vii
Editorial preface   ix
Acknowledgements   xi

1 FAILURE TO THRIVE RESEARCH AND PRACTICE: SETTING THE SCENE   1

Introduction   1
Short history of the understanding of FTT   2
Current thinking on FTT   3
Classification of FTT and feeding disorders   5
Definitions of FTT   5
     Case Study 1: Amina, a child falling through centile lines yet not
     reaching the 3rd centile   7
Methodological problems in FTT research   14
Methodology used in this review   16
Differences of view between professions   17

2 WHY FTT IS IMPORTANT: IDENTIFICATION, PREVALENCE AND EFFECTS   19

Identification   19
Prevalence   21
Effects of FTT   23
     Case Study 2: Kieron and the effects of FTT   24
     Case Study 3: The impact of Saul's FTT on family dynamics   30
Summary   32

3   CAUSAL FACTORS IN FTT   34

Organic *vs* non-organic   34
Failure to thrive and abuse or neglect   35
An interactional perspective on FTT   39
Child factors in FTT   41
   Case Study 4: Child and family factors resulting in failure to thrive   41
Mother/carer factors in FTT   47
Conclusion   54
Summary   54

4   INTERVENTIONS FOR FTT AND FEEDING PROBLEMS: WHAT WORKS?   56

Preliminary notes on the intervention studies   57
Overviews and summaries of FTT research and clinical practice   58
Growth outcomes from FTT intervention studies   60
Cognitive development outcomes from FTT intervention studies   65
Feeding disorders studies   66
Summary   72

5   MODELS OF INTERVENTION: WHERE, HOW AND BY WHOM?   73

Where to treat: Home, clinic or hospital?   73
How to treat: Parents' experiences of FTT interventions   76
   Case Study 5: Parents' experiences of FTT interventions   78
Who should treat: The case for multidisciplinary work   79
A model for effective FTT intervention   82
Summary   89

6   CONCLUSIONS AND RECOMMENDATIONS   91

Key issues   91
Developing best practice   94
Recommendations   100

APPENDIX: RESEARCH STUDIES OF INTERVENTION PROGRAMMES   101

References   115

Index   123

FOREWORD

'You can't take the whole population of Glasgow into care.' This was the comment of a participant at the first meeting I ever attended on failure to thrive in 1987, where removal from the home was the only treatment mentioned. We left that meeting already planning a community-based treatment programme for failure to thrive. What we did not realise was that during that process our understanding of the condition would be so utterly transformed.

It could be argued that research findings over the last ten years have mainly taught us what failure to thrive is *not*. This book outlines comprehensively the research evidence that has led us to understand that, rather than a sinister condition confined to the poorest and most negligent families, failure to thrive is in fact a common condition of early childhood that can occur in any home.

Similarly, failure to thrive is not a disease or a syndrome, but simply a description of children at one extreme of the normal range for weight gain. How then should we decide where normality ends and FTT begins? While there is no absolute answer to this, we now know much more about the range of normal weight gain and can apply consistent growth-based diagnostic criteria. Despite this, inconsistent and subjective diagnostic approaches are often used, resulting in the stigmatising of already disadvantaged families while other children remain undetected and unhelped.

While FTT may simply represent one end of the normal range, that is not to say that it does not matter. Slow weight gain casts a long shadow in terms of growth and development and may cause great anguish to parents. Some of this distress may flow from the management offered which varies greatly between disciplines and around the country. All too often no intervention as such is attempted: a child may for example be weighed regularly and tested for every possible rare medical disorder and yet never receive any sort of dietetic advice.

But what treatment should be offered? Over time the majority of FTT children will improve but there is reasonable evidence now that supportive treatments speed that process. Having attempted both hospital and community-based management, it is clear to me that treatment should ideally be both home based and multidisciplinary in nature. However, this can be an expensive option, unless imaginative use is made of a range of skills and levels of expertise and duplication is avoided. Jane Batchelor has reviewed the range of treatments that have been described in the literature and summarises their key messages succinctly. She also discusses the practicalities of establishing effective and efficient services using perennially limited resources.

It is not always clear by what exact mechanism treatments succeed. Families are mysterious organisms and successful management requires the acceptance of uncertainty and a lack of direct control. At the same time one must retain a clear-sighted, objective view of progress. If a child shows rapid catch-up weight gain as a result of regular visits from a nursery nurse, we will not know exactly what has changed for the better, just that something has. Conversely if a family report greatly improved eating behaviour, yet the child remains markedly underweight with no catch-up, you may not know exactly *why* this is, but you do know that this child must in fact still be eating too little for his or her needs.

This volume has drawn together a wide range of research evidence in order to explore the complex interactions and dynamics that may combine to cause and perpetuate failure to thrive. Many uncertainties remain: why do some children falter in their growth, whilst most do not? Why do some recover quickly while others show no response despite every sort of intervention? There are questions still to be answered, but in the meantime families need help and professional staff want to offer the best there is available. This book offers many clues to this puzzling condition and unravels the confusions that have grown up around it. It will be a valuable resource for everyone involved in the care of children with failure to thrive, from student practitioner to specialist.

CHARLOTTE WRIGHT
Senior Lecturer
Department of Child Health, University of Newcastle

EDITORIAL PREFACE

Recognition and understanding of failure to thrive (FTT) in young children has developed considerably since The Children's Society began its work in this field in the early 1990s. Continuing study has led to a change in the earlier belief that FTT was solely the result of either organic disorder or maternal deprivation or child abuse. It is now widely accepted that large numbers of children – as many as 5 per cent of the under-5 population – from across the social spectrum are affected and that feeding difficulties are the major contributory factor.

Despite the prevalence of the problem there is no universal provision to ensure that families throughout the country have access to a service that could help them to resolve the difficulties contributing to their child's failure to thrive.

As The Children's Society's work became increasingly well known, the team received contacts from families and health and social care professionals throughout the United Kingdom (and beyond) looking for information about where they could go for help in their locality. This difficulty in establishing just where FTT services were sited was one with which we had become very familiar. In order to develop its own work the team had attempted to learn about the work others were undertaking with regard to this issue. It very quickly became evident that there was no quick or easy way to do this.

Jane Batchelor at the University of Bath was commissioned to undertake a review of the current state of play within the FTT field. This would provide a baseline of information, which could then be extended and updated, and also give an indication of the whereabouts of existing services.

The Children's Society has developed the Feeding Matters National Programme with a view to contributing to and progressing the debate and understandings about FTT. The focus of the Society's own work in the field will be the National Development Centre based in Bristol which is supported by the direct experience of our practice bases.

DI HAMPTON
Feeding Matters National Development Centre
The Children's Society

ACKNOWLEDGEMENTS

The author would like to thank Di Hampton of The Children's Society for provision of the material for the case studies. The studies presented are all composite case studies based on the extensive experience of Di Hampton and her colleagues in their work with FTT children and their families.

The author would also like to thank the many practitioners, researchers and academics in the field of failure to thrive who responded to her enquiries about current practice.

The Children's Society would like to thank the Child Growth Foundation for permission to use their growth charts (Figs 2 and 3), for which disks were supplied by Harlow Printing, Maxwell Street, South Shields NE33 4PU. Thanks also to Castlemead Publications for permission to use their growth chart (Fig. 1).

The Children's Society would also like to thank the members of the Publications Advisory Group for their valued advice: Kathy Aubeelack; Nicola Baboneau; Ron Chopping (Chair); Annabelle Dixon; Sara Fielden; Judy Foster; Christopher Walsh.

1

FAILURE TO THRIVE RESEARCH AND PRACTICE
SETTING THE SCENE

Introduction

The growth of young children has always concerned parents. When a child is born, most of us ask the question, 'Girl or boy?' followed by, 'How much did s/he weigh?' Progress reports to family and friends often include comments on the baby's weight gain, and health checks at baby clinics usually include regular weighing. So it is not surprising that slow or failing growth is a source of anxiety to parents and professionals alike.

Academics, researchers and practitioners in the fields of health and social care have been concerned about failure to thrive (FTT) for decades. Over that time, there have been important developments in our understanding of the condition, what causes it and how it might be treated. In recent years there has been heightened interest, fuelled perhaps by two developments. Firstly there is a growing recognition that health and illness in later life is partly determined by our health status in very early childhood (Barker, 1991). Secondly, there has been a renewed interest in the topic of neglect, with which failure to thrive is often associated in the minds of some professionals.

The aim of this review is to bring together in one book these recent developments in identification of failure to thrive in young children and to evaluate intervention strategies currently in use. There have been numerous papers published over the past ten years on the topic of failure to thrive and the associated field of feeding disorders, some of which report findings from intervention programmes. There are also a number of review articles and papers drawing together various approaches to treatment, intervention or resolution, some of which propose models to guide the development of intervention or treatment strategies. Findings from recent research studies of failure to thrive interventions summarised here range from single clinical cases through to extensive randomised trials, including some summary papers that bring together models of 'good practice'.

The starting point here is a brief history of the understanding of failure to thrive, followed by current thinking on FTT and an examination of definitions. This chapter then moves on to address methodological problems in existing failure to thrive research and describes the methodology adopted for this review. It concludes with a discussion of the differences in view of the different professions working with FTT children and their families. This opening chapter provides a backdrop for the following chapters which address: identification, prevalence and effects of failure to thrive; the aetiology of failure to thrive; a review of failure to thrive and feeding disorders treatment studies; and proposed models for intervention. The final chapter discusses issues arising from the book, how to develop best practice in the current context, and concludes with a list of recommendations. This is followed by an appendix with full details of the research studies of intervention programmes cited in the book.

Throughout the review the initials FTT will generally be used to stand for the term 'failure to thrive'; this is common in the literature in this field.

Short history of the understanding of FTT

Within the developing world, failure to thrive is synonymous with malnutrition and physical, material and economic deprivation. However, within the Western world it has been assumed for many decades that poverty has been eradicated. In this context, failure to thrive has long been understood to be the result of circumstances other than material deprivation. At the beginning of this century the term 'failure to thrive' was first used to describe children reared in foundling homes who received poor caretaking and who were prone to grow poorly (Wolke, 1996). The term gained currency throughout the 1940s and 1950s as studies of poorly growing children in institutional care proliferated. It was suggested that such children received adequate calories but grew poorly because they were deprived of stimulation by their caretakers (Spitz, 1945, cited by Wolke, 1996).

Failure to thrive was considered to be the consequence of one of two possible sets of circumstances: either

■   there was an organic cause such as an illness; or

■   the child was suffering from non-organic failure to thrive due to emotional deprivation in general and maternal deprivation in particular.

So FTT was attributed either to organic or non-organic causes, as if they were always mutually exclusive, and the non-organic cause was assumed to be emotional deprivation. This understanding drove the research agenda through the 1950s as researchers attempted to make sense of the mechanisms by which children consumed calories but failed to grow. For example, it was thought that emotional deprivation could lead to short stature by means of abnormality of endocrine function, diminished intestinal absorption or inefficient utilisation of energy (Skuse *et al.*, 1994b).

The shifts in understanding of FTT over the past forty years are well summarised by Skuse *et al.* (1994b). Whitten *et al.* (1969) tested in the 1960s the hypothesis that growth failure in psychosocial adversity was due to inadequate energy intake and concluded that the infants in their study were underweight because they were under-eating. This important finding shifted the main FTT research agenda away from abuse and deprivation towards nutrition and malnutrition (Skuse *et al.*, 1994b; Wolke, 1996), certainly in relation to young children (under the age of 2 years) who fail to thrive.

Whilst insufficient intake of calories as the cause of non-organic FTT was gradually accepted, many persisted in the view that this inadequate intake was due to parental (particularly maternal) deprivation. So, until the mid-1980s, nearly all FTT research continued to focus on maternal deprivation, on the assumption that it was distorted mother–child relationships which led mothers to feed their infants insufficient calories for adequate growth.

Current thinking on FTT

The view that mothers of FTT children provide them with too few calories has persisted in some quarters, partly due to the fact that much research was and continues to be based on clinical samples. Such samples will be heavily biased towards children who are neglected or are receiving seriously inadequate parenting.

Epidemiological studies undertaken in the 1980s and 1990s (e.g. Skuse *et al.*, 1994b; Wilensky *et al.*, 1996) have taken forward our understanding of prevalence rates of FTT and have helped put the clinical findings of distorted or neglectful mother–child relationships into perspective. Whilst such difficulties will occur in the families of some FTT children, it is now known that this is rare: with few exceptions, mother–infant interaction has not been found to be poorer in the families of FTT children than in that of controls (Wolke, 1996).

Recent FTT research has been more sophisticated, moving away from assumptions of a simple 'cause and effect' model. There is increasing use of an interactional perspective, in which researchers explore the multiplicity of factors which, individually and together, might result in a child failing to thrive. For example, some research has focused on the part an infant plays in the process of failure to thrive by virtue of its temperament or because of a feeding skills disorder. The association between feeding difficulties and FTT was identified as early as 1976. Research over the past decade has increasingly addressed the process of feeding, including the ways in which even mild oral-motor dysfunction might predispose an infant to failure to thrive.

Whether a child consumes sufficient calories will then depend largely upon the resources of caregivers who are responsible for feeding. Do the caregivers know what a child needs in the diet to achieve normal growth? Do they have the skills to feed a cranky or sleepy child? Do they have the physical and emotional energy required to persevere? Last but not least, do they have the material resources to provide an appropriate level of nutrition? The way that poverty affects families with young children, in terms of provision of an adequate diet when on an inadequate income, is now receiving more attention from researchers. Such questions are also increasingly being addressed by practitioners at the assessment stage of FTT intervention programmes, as will be seen in the following chapters.

In parallel to these developments, there has been a growing acceptance that it is of limited value to think of FTT as either organic or non-organic in origin. Whilst for some children there may be an organic factor which contributes to their failing to thrive, this does not preclude non-organic factors from playing a part. It is generally accepted that there are many factors which might contribute to one child's failure to thrive and that assessment and intervention need to take account of this multifactorial aetiology.

Classification of FTT and feeding disorders

Whilst there is some overlap between failure to thrive and feeding disorders, the terms are sometimes used inappropriately, as if they are synonymous and interchangeable. This blurring or confusion of terms is compounded by the lack of a validated classification system for FTT. Since 1994 the US *Diagnostic and Statistical Manual* (American Psychiatric Association, 1994) has included the category of feeding disorder of early childhood for use in classifying infants whose failure to eat sufficiently has had a significant impact on body mass (Hakim-Larson *et al.*, 1997). Similarly, the WHO classification of mental and behavioural disorders (World Health Organisation, 1992) includes feeding disorders in early infancy and childhood. It suggests that the disorder should be diagnosed if feeding difficulties are beyond the normal range and result in a child failing to gain weight or losing weight over a period of at least one month. It should be remembered that, although a feeding disorder may result in or contribute to a child failing to thrive, either might exist without the other (Benoit, 1993).

Definitions of FTT

Failure to thrive is commonly defined in terms of poor or failing physical growth, sometimes accompanied by delay in other areas of development. However, there have been differing views as to what constitutes 'poor' or 'failing' growth. Traditionally FTT had been defined as a fall below the 3rd (now 2nd) centile for weight by a child whose prior growth trajectory took them along a higher centile line.

For many years, charts used in the UK were those based on work by Tanner and Whitehouse (1959); they have recently been revised by Buckler and Tanner (see Fig. 1, pp. 8–9). Using data from a number of large-scale studies of children's growth and development, they constructed boys' and girls' growth centile charts for plotting weight, height and head circumference over time. The weight centile charts have ages (in weeks and then months up to 24 months, then in months and years to age 16) along their horizontal axes, and weight in kilograms on the vertical axes. Those based on Tanner's work have the 3rd, 10th, 50th, 90th and 97th centiles printed onto the charts. Each line is drawn on the basis of weight-for-age data for girls (or boys) from large-scale studies. For example, the 3rd centile line on the chart for girls shown in Fig. 1 connects the points at which, at each age, only 3 per cent of girls were below that weight and 97 per cent were above, whilst the 90th centile line connects those points at which only 10 per cent were above the weight and 90 per cent were below.

Charting of children's growth has been refined over recent years, partly as a result of criticisms of the data upon which the Tanner and Whitehouse charts were based. One development has been the new British Standards – the 9-centile growth charts illustrated in Fig. 2. These are generally perceived as more appropriate than the old charts (Savage *et al.*, 1996) and are now commonly used in child health clinics and as parent-held records. They are based on more representative data on growth and are recommended by the Department of Health (1996).

In recent years the definition of FTT as a fall below the 3rd centile for weight has been criticised as too narrow. It fails to capture large children who may drop across several centile lines but never be below the 3rd. For example, Amina, the child described in Case Study 1, started life on the 75th centile, as shown on her first weight chart (Fig. 3). She had progressed close to this line but then dropped to the 25th centile at the age of 15 months, as shown on her second chart. She would not be picked up as failing to thrive if the definition was a fall below the 3rd centile.

A definition of FTT as a fall below the 3rd centile is also open to criticism as it is inappropriately reliant upon charts which are known to have their limitations. For example, they do not allow for the fact that children who are heavy at birth will tend to drift down the centile chart over time, without necessarily failing to thrive. The normal process of growth in early childhood is now known to include the potential for variation in centile position, growth faltering, and fluctuation of weight while still remaining within normal limits (Wright, 1995). Not all children who deviate from an established centile will be failing to thrive.

So relying on centile charts will not only result in some FTT children being missed, but also in some children with normal variations in growth being wrongly identified as failing to thrive. For example, Wright (1995) cites earlier work by Edwards *et al.* (1990) who had used a drop across two centile lines after the 6-week weight as the criterion for FTT. By their definition, 22 per cent of the children in Wright's study area were found to have suffered a period of FTT. Close examination by Wright of the Tanner and Whitehouse standards revealed that the great majority of children show a rise in centile position in the early weeks of life. This is followed by an average fall of one centile between 3 and 6 months. This led Wright to recognise that those standards were inherently inaccurate in that age range and that there was a need for further work to establish a definition of abnormality.

Wright and colleagues have since developed the Thrive Index, and have selected as their screening threshold that value which screens in the slowest growing 5 per cent of children (Wright *et al.*, 1994a; Wright, 1995). The Thrive Index is a measure of discrepancy between a child's predicted and actual growth in terms of weight gain. The Index allows for the tendency for very large and small infants to move inwards towards the average (Wright *et al.*, 1994a). They found that 80 per cent of children aged 18–30 months in

Case study 1

Amina, a child falling through centile lines yet not reaching the 3rd centile

The centile chart (see Fig. 3) tracks the faltering weight of Amina aged 15 months. As the chart shows, by 8 weeks of age her growth curve had been established along the 75th centile. She successfully maintained this position until she was 10 months old. The beginning of the downturn in her growth trajectory coincided with her having a bout of flu. Over the next few months Amina's weight slipped to the 25th centile.

Her parents reported a number of concerns in addition to her faltering weight. Amina was getting noticeably thinner; she had lost her chubby 'baby' look; she often seemed lethargic and lacking in energy; and people had begun to comment on her pale complexion and the dark circles around her eyes. Most worrying from the parents' point of view was the fact that it had become increasingly difficult to persuade Amina to eat what they considered to be a reasonable amount of food.

Despite the fact that Amina's weight was still well above the 3rd centile, she was displaying a number of indicators of failure to thrive.

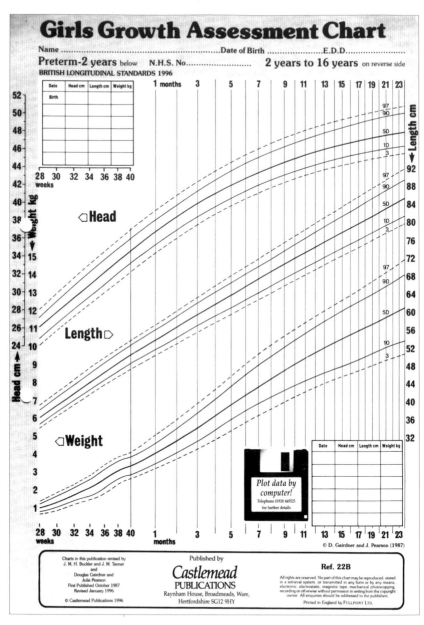

Fig. 1 Buckler and Tanner growth assessment charts for girls, birth to 2 years (above), and 2–16 years (opposite). Charts no longer in general usage within the UK. Reproduced with the permission of the copyright holders, Castlemead Publications.

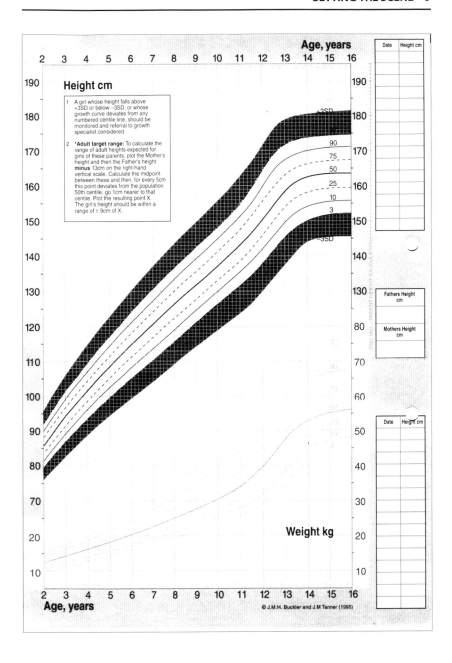

Age, years

Height cm

1 A girl whose height falls above
+3SD or below −3SD, or whose
growth curve deviates from any
numbered centile line, should be
monitored and referral to growth
specialist considered.

2 *Adult target range: To calculate the
range of adult heights expected for
girls of these parents, plot the Mother's
height and then the Father's height
minus 13cm on the right-hand
vertical scale. Calculate the midpoint
between these and then, for every 5cm
this point deviates from the population
50th centile, go 1cm nearer to that
centile. Plot the resulting point X.
The girl's height should be within a
range of ± 9cm of X.

Weight kg

Age, years

© J.M.H. Buckler and J.M Tanner (1995)

Date | Height cm

Fathers Height
cm

Mothers Height
cm

Date | Height cm

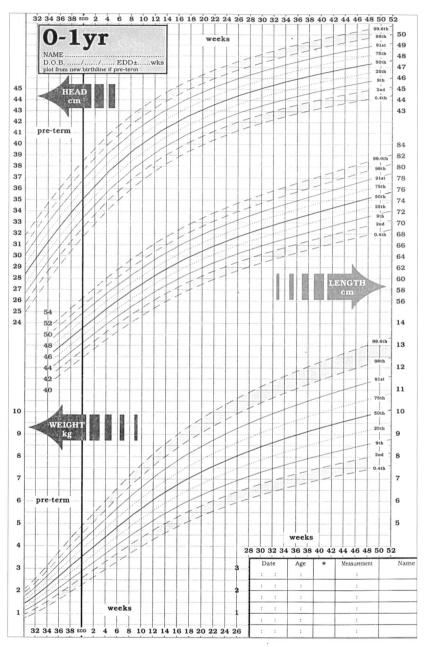

Fig. 2   Child Growth Foundation charts for boys, 0–1 year (above), and 1–5 years (opposite). © Child Growth Foundation.

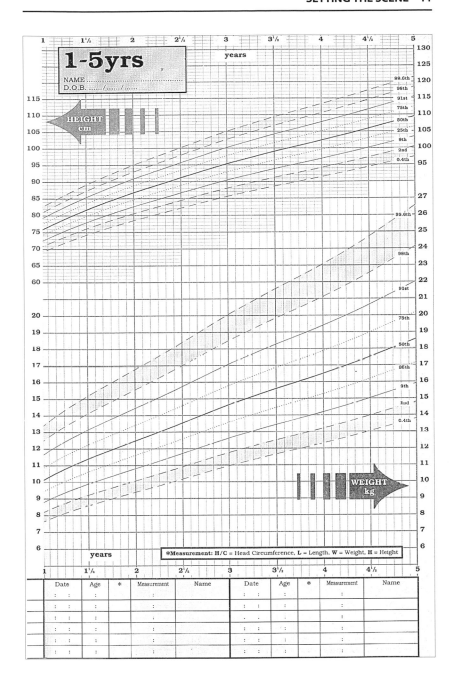

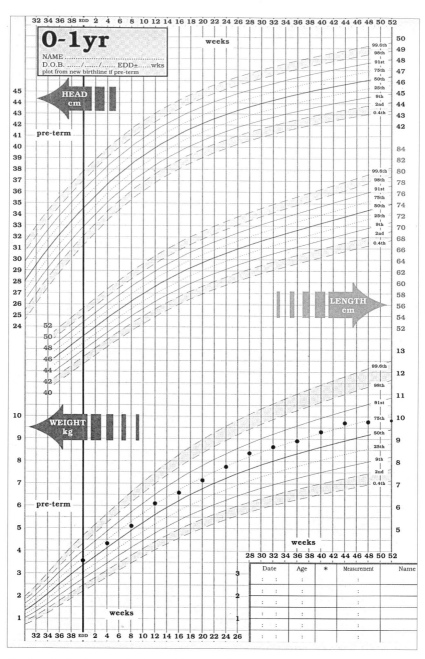

Fig. 3   Amina's growth charts (above and opposite), showing the downturn in her growth curve on the second chart. Charts © Child Growth Foundation.

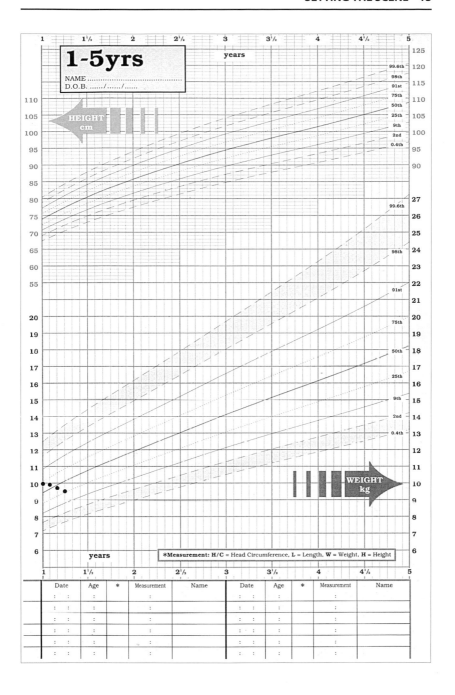

their study area had adequate records for their Thrive Index to be calculated, suggesting that general use of such an index is feasible. They found no evidence that the adequacy of records differed by level of deprivation but rather that inadequate weight data was primarily due to missing records. All the children falling below the screening threshold are now included in their longitudinal survey of weight faltering in early childhood in Newcastle, known as the Parkin Project (Wright, 1995).

Recently Wright and colleagues have developed and evaluated charts designed to monitor children who have already been identified as slow weight-gainers (Wright, 1995; Wright *et al.*, 1994a, 1998a); these charts are commercially available and are in use in some areas. This work has been only one of many developments in recent years regarding charting of children's growth (Lucas *et al.*, 1986; Cole, 1995, 1997; Freeman *et al.*, 1995).

The old centile charts had their limitations and a narrow definition of FTT as a drop below the 3rd centile for weight was a crude measure of growth. However, such tools had the advantage of being widely accepted and understood by the various health and social care professionals involved in monitoring children's growth and development. Recent developments in charting children are to be welcomed, particularly if they result in more accurate and speedy identification of abnormal variations in growth. However, the proliferation of charts available could serve to compound problems of definition and hence identification of FTT, unless there is some standardisation of practice.

Methodological problems in FTT research

There are major methodological problems within FTT research, discussed in recent years by many working in this field (Drotar, 1990, 1994; Skuse *et al.*, 1994b; Wolke, 1996). These difficulties can in part be explained as a consequence of the many causal factors which may contribute to a child failing to thrive, as discussed above. The methodological problems plaguing FTT research, whether aimed at establishing incidence rates or evaluating interventions, are then exacerbated by the use of widely different definitions of failure to thrive. This point is well illustrated by Wilcox *et al.* (1989) who reviewed 22 current paediatric texts and 13 journal articles on FTT and found only nine texts and nine articles that described FTT in quantitative terms and even these lacked consensus.

As discussed earlier, until the mid-1980s nearly all FTT research focused on maternal deprivation as a causal factor. However, interpretations of the early studies were often dubious. They usually only used clinical samples or case studies, yet results have been extrapolated to the full FTT population. One recent review of the literature (Wolke, 1996) showed that only 10 per cent of publications on FTT up to that time were based on empirical literature.

With studies of hospitalised samples in particular, great caution should be exercised over generalising findings to the full FTT population. Boddy and Skuse (1994), in their excellent overview, stress that hospital-referred cases give a highly selective sample. This point has since been reiterated by Wilensky and his colleagues who write:

> The picture of major psychosocial dysfunction in many of the [failure to thrive] hospital inpatients may reflect a selection bias and not necessarily characterise the profile of cases being managed in the paediatrician's office without ever requiring hospital admission. (Wilensky et al., 1996, p. 145)

As early as 1988, attention was drawn to the inadequacies of studies looking at the outcome of FTT interventions (Drotar, 1988). Where children are identified as failing to thrive, methodological problems may arise in relation to the tools used to assess them and hence for plans for subsequent intervention. For example, recently nutritionists have identified problems with studies that include dietary assessments, because details of such assessments are often missing, making an informed interpretation of the results difficult (Nelson et al., 1993).

Much FTT research can also be criticised as being gender-blind. It purports to address parenting but usually only studies mother–child interactions and behaviours. Such shortcomings are not unusual in health and social care research: recent child protection research (Department of Health, 1995) has been criticised on the same basis (Parton, 1996).

In summary, there is strong evidence that FTT studies based on clinical samples are biased due to the nature of the sample. Such bias potentially perpetuates the myth of maternal deprivation as the cause of FTT. In addition, any treatment or intervention programme developed on the basis of findings from such clinical samples may give only a partial and distorted picture. If such programmes only have referred to them those cases from one part of the FTT spectrum, there is a risk that treatment will develop along lines appropriate for those referred but less so for those not referred – those whose FTT has a different aetiology and hence requires a different type of intervention.

Methodology used in this review

For the purposes of this review, an attempt has been made to cover major developments in Britain, supplemented by some material from other parts of Europe, North America, Canada and Australasia. The main source of material has been research or evaluation studies published between 1988 and 1998.

Published papers on FTT were located through systematic searches of standard databases covering academic and professional work in this field. The search for papers was extended beyond the specific 'failure to thrive' literature and encompassed to a limited extent research in the field of feeding disorders in young children since the two conditions often (but not always) overlap. However, this review is not an exhaustive study of all materials in or relating to the field of failure to thrive; nor can it be described as truly systematic.

It should be remembered that various factors come into play when undertaking a literature review in a multidisciplinary field such as failure to thrive. Some professions working in this field (notably the medical profession) have a stronger culture and tradition than others (for example, social work) of undertaking clinical research that culminates in publications. Hence this review may overemphasise the medical perspective at the expense of others, since primary sources of material were the professional and academic journals.

In an attempt to address this possible bias and build a rounded picture of recent developments in FTT intervention or treatment, the literature review has been supplemented by information provided by a sample of current practitioners. The reasons for establishing such contacts were twofold. Firstly, as stated above, some professions have a stronger culture of research and publication than others. Secondly, there is always a time lag between work in hand and publication in professional or academic journals.

Various strategies were employed to build a picture of recent developments. Letters were sent to all who had contacted the author over the past year for an offprint of a recent FTT article; they spanned Europe, North

America and Canada. Contacts provided by The Children's Society Feeding Matters national programme were followed up (usually by letter then telephone call). The author also followed up her own links with practitioners in the local area. A few contacts were made with clinicians who had published studies in which reference was made to further ongoing work; this included Ramsay (in Canada), Iwaniec (in Northern Ireland) and Harris (UK).

Other links were made by making selective use of the attendance list of a recent national conference on FTT. Brief items about the work were inserted in various professional journals and newsletters in the UK. The Internet was used to seek out contacts and locate publications. One entry on the Internet from a family who had experienced the trauma of a diagnosis of FTT was a valuable example of 'user feedback', generally lacking elsewhere.

Over forty contacts were made with current practitioners and researchers. Some were just a letter or e-mail response whilst others resulted in telephone interviews. The disciplines and professions covered included health visitors, dietitians, paediatricians, family centre workers, psychologists, clinical nurse specialists and managers, and various individuals such as the manager of a nursery, a child protection manager, a member of a voluntary self-help organisation, a social work academic and a chief executive of a national voluntary organisation. The geographical spread was wide: contacts were made with practitioners across all of England (from the south coast to Newcastle), Wales and Northern Ireland (although none in Scotland) as well as parts of North America.

Whilst the responses received are in no way a representative sample, the views of these workers and information they gave regarding the development (or decline) of services for FTT children are used to illustrate the following discussion and to inform conclusions drawn regarding the way forward.

Differences of view between professions

The multifactorial aetiology of failure to thrive raises particular issues, not only in terms of locating relevant material for a review but also in terms of pulling it together. The professional perspective of those working with FTT children inevitably shapes their understanding of causal factors (including influencing what is even considered a potential causal factor). This in turn will shape the model(s) of intervention developed and used.

The apocryphal story of six blind men and an elephant comes to mind. Each touched a different part of the creature and so each 'saw' it differently, depending on whether they took hold of the tail, tusk, trunk, ear or body. In a way each was right in their description, yet the whole was not any one part; indeed it was more than the sum of the parts. The same may be said of failure to thrive. There are many aspects to the condition and many routes to it. To some extent each worker in the field of FTT will have their view of the condition, its aetiology and appropriate interventions, shaped by their professional focus and understanding. As a result they may only see that part which equates with their view; that part which they can see through their 'window'.

The language used in discussing a topic both reflects and shapes our position and values regarding that subject. As described above, there are important differences of view between professions (and sometimes within professions) as to what 'failure to thrive' is. Much of the literature drawn upon in this review is from the medical profession. As such, it is often framed in terms of a medical model that comprises 'diagnosis' followed by 'treatment' or 'management'. Other professions, such as psychology and social work, may view problems and ways to overcome them from a different perspective. Their approach may be more collaborative. This difference is then reflected in the language used: rather than 'treatment' they may use terms such as 'working towards a resolution', or 'intervening'. Even the language and understanding relating to abuse and neglect varies: for example, members of the medical profession may use the term 'abuse' in a way which is not meant to convey any notion of intent, but instead simply reflects the fact that a child's body has been subjected to a physiological insult.

These differences in use of language, and the differences in professional understanding and perspective which they reflect, need to be borne in mind in the coming chapters, as do the methodological problems and research shortcomings identified earlier.

2

WHY FTT IS IMPORTANT
IDENTIFICATION, PREVALENCE AND EFFECTS

Identification

The discussion in the previous chapter highlighted the way in which the beliefs which professionals hold about failure to thrive will influence their identification (or not) of the condition. Identification of FTT will in turn have an impact upon the treatment provided or the interventions developed.

Comprehensive identification of children who are failing to thrive can only fully be achieved by thorough screening programmes, with all young children having their growth recorded onto appropriate charts. However, there is considerable evidence that charting has tended in the past only to be undertaken to confirm a professional's prior assessment of a child as failing to thrive, rather than as a tool for identifying FTT children (Batchelor and Kerslake, 1990).

Other researchers have since commented on the lack of importance often attached to weight data by primary health care staff. On the basis of her research findings, Wright observed, 'Many GP practices had beautifully kept weight records' but centile charts were often not filled in. She also noted the difficulties experienced in obtaining a good level of returns of children's weights from health visitors, for use in her weight surveillance programme (Wright, 1995). Of the first 50 cases identified as growth faltering by means of the Thrive Index (see p. 7), 13 children were unknown by health visitors to be growing poorly. These children might never have been identified by their primary health care workers as failing to thrive.

This failure to undertake weight surveillance or charting of all children may be understood in terms of professional preconceptions about FTT. Some professionals view FTT as being, by definition, due either to an organic cause (such as an undiagnosed disease) or to neglect, abuse or deprivation. From this perspective, any child meeting FTT threshold criteria, yet not presenting as, say, deprived and not having an obvious organic basis for their delayed growth, must have been wrongly labelled as failing to thrive (Wright, 1995, p. 84).

In an earlier study, Batchelor and Kerslake (1990) had similarly noted that certain children were often diagnosed by health professionals as 'small', regardless of their earlier growth status and the size of their parents. These were children for whom no organic basis for their failure to thrive could be found, and factors associated with poverty and deprivation were not present. Other children with poor weight gain passed unrecognised as such by their health visitors, despite the fact that they were regularly weighed. It seemed that children who appeared to be well-cared for and who were not ill were excluded from being considered as failing to thrive. In such circum-stances charts were often not completed, although weights were recorded on clinic notes. Charting often appeared to be used as a means of demon-strating or evidencing a prior diagnosis of failure to thrive (made on the basis of poor growth plus neglect or deprivation), rather than as a tool for identifying every child's growth pattern and so diagnosing FTT in any child, regardless of the presence or absence of evidence of neglect or of an organic cause such as undiagnosed illness.

In fact there is evidence to suggest that only about 5 per cent of young children with inexplicable poor growth are found to have a previously undiagnosed illness, and only a small minority are failing to thrive because of abuse or neglect (Boddy and Skuse, 1994; Skuse *et al.*, 1994a; Wright and Talbot, 1996). For the majority of FTT children, their poor or failing growth is due to one or more of a range of factors including parental lack of knowl-edge of nutritional requirements, feeding difficulties, and lack of resources (financial, personal or emotional) to meet the needs of a particular child.

The preceding discussion nicely illustrates the way in which professional beliefs may influence identification, which in turn further influences the way the condition is defined and the extent to which it is identified and then treated. This takes us on to issues of prevalence of failure to thrive.

Prevalence

As discussed above, prevalence rates will depend firstly upon the definition of FTT used. If the criterion for FTT is a weight below the 3rd centile, it is not surprising that epidemiological studies identify around 3 per cent of children as failing to thrive. Of greater interest are the variations found between predicted incidence of FTT (which is largely an artefact of the weight criterion) and rates based on levels of identification by health and social care professionals. This takes one back to the issues of charting practices and professional interpretations or beliefs regarding FTT. It is therefore not surprising that widely different figures have been proposed over the years for prevalence rates of FTT. These variations in rates are compounded by such methodological problems as over-reliance upon clinical samples.

A valuable series of epidemiological studies on individual and environmental variables associated with failure to thrive has been undertaken in the UK since the early 1980s (Skuse et al., 1992, 1994a, b; Wolke, 1996). The definition for FTT used in these studies was a weight-for-age Z score below −1.88 (which approximates to being below the 3rd centile) attained by the age of 12 months and sustained for 3 months or more.

The studies of Skuse and his colleagues provide valuable data on the growth of infants. From 1554 potential subjects, there were 52 confirmed cases of growth faltering under the age of 12 months, giving an incidence of 3.3 per cent. Wilensky et al. (1996) have since used the same criteria in their community-based study in Israel and found similar prevalence rates. Their study was carried out by means of a retrospective review of records held in maternal and child health clinics of a community-based cohort of all infants born in 1991. They found 3.9 per cent of infants were failing to thrive.

It can be assumed that the children screened by Skuse and his colleagues were broadly in the same socio-economic group, since they all lived within one disadvantaged inner city health district. It is interesting that, despite this homogeneity, the researchers noted considerable but unexplained differences between ethnic groups in terms of incidence of FTT. This suggests that there is more work to be done on incidence rates across different ethnic groups, which might in turn help develop our understanding of causal factors (addressed in the next chapter).

Some studies have looked at environmental factors which might be associated with increased rates of FTT. Wright *et al.* (1994b) used child health records for a cohort of children. They classified the children's level of deprivation (as affluent, intermediate or deprived) by means of census data for area of residence. They concluded that deprived children were more likely than intermediate children to have failure to thrive but that it occurred across all three groups. They unexpectedly found that children from affluent areas showed increased rates of FTT. They suggest that this may be due to higher rates of breast-feeding, as some infants continued to be breast-fed beyond the point when breast milk alone was sufficient to meet their growth needs. More recently Wright (1995) has developed a Thrive Index to screen for slow weight gain and has analysed the first 50 cases of FTT identified within selected GP practices in Newcastle. Most of these cases were not from deprived parts of the city. Overt neglect was rare but 38 of the 50 children, although living in apparently caring homes, showed evidence of undernutrition.

These findings mirror those from the earlier work of Batchelor and Kerslake (1990). They found that, out of every three young children whose clinic weights took them below the 3rd centile when plotted onto weight charts, one passed unrecognised as a poor weight gainer by their health visitor. Subsequent work by Batchelor (1996) showed much better rates of identification, with primary health care staff having expressed concern about the growth of four out of every five children who had dropped below the 3rd centile. These figures are close to those of Wright and Talbot (1996) who also found that, for every five children identified by their screening threshold as FTT, four were already known by their health visitor to be growing poorly.

However, when Batchelor (1996) broadened her criteria for FTT and examined the records of those children who had dropped across two major centile lines (albeit not below the third), she found that half of these children were not recognised by their primary health care worker as poor weight gainers. As stated earlier, several of the children in Wright's study were considered by their health visitors as wrongly labelled as FTT through screening, although they were subsequently found to have real problems. This highlights the extent to which FTT prevalence rates calculated on the basis of identification by health or social care professionals will be an underestimation, since those identified and referred are those on whom the professionals are prepared to put the label 'failure to thrive'.

Effects of FTT

Effects on the child

Whilst it has been established that failure to thrive exists, the next question must be 'Does this matter?' Failure to thrive could just be a troublesome condition which causes carers and health professionals much concern but does not have any consequences in terms of the child's development.

The evidence is mounting regarding the long-term effects of FTT. Recent studies have focused more clearly on the effects, taking care to test such factors as children's developmental quotient, with tests administered and scored by raters who are blind to the case/control status of each child (Skuse *et al.*, 1994a; Wilensky *et al.*, 1996). Wolke (1994) summarises much of the evidence and concludes that FTT children as a group have cognitive abilities 1–1.5 standard deviations below population or control group means.

Reif *et al.* (1995) followed up 61 FTT infants five years after their initial presentation. Compared to a control group matched for age, sex, social class and ethnicity, the index group of children were shorter, gained less weight, had more learning difficulties and evidenced developmental delay.

Case Study 2 on pp. 24–25 illustrates the way in which delayed development is often noticed early by parents, and may be one of the factors which prompts them to seek professional help or advice.

A significant correlation has been found between IQ outcome and severity of FTT (Wright, 1995; Corbett *et al.*, 1996). Similarly Wilensky *et al.* (1996) report significantly lower mental development scores for FTT children than matched controls at age 20 months. It is thought that undernutrition depresses the rate of all brain growth processes contemporaneous with it.

However, not all of the evidence on the effects of FTT is clear-cut. Puckering *et al.* (1995) analysed data relating to 23 children who showed stunted growth but were otherwise healthy. They reported on the children's cognitive development and found it was significantly retarded relative to a matched comparison group. They analysed transcripts of verbal and

Case study 2

Kieron and the effects of FTT

Kieron was the fourth of five children in his family. However, the feeding problems encountered with him were not something his parents had experienced with any of their other children. Richard and Sarah found it difficult to identify just when things began to go wrong, but over a period of weeks they gradually realised that Kieron was eating less and less. By the time he was 16 months old they also noticed that he had begun refusing to eat things which he had previously enjoyed. Kieron's older brothers and sister had noticed that he was 'playing up' at the table and began to comment on his behaviour and the amount he was (or was not) eating. He also seemed to be losing weight: his eldest brother George pointed to Kieron's 'sticking out bones' (his ribs) when they shared a bath.

As an experienced mother, Sarah tried a number of different tactics to try to persuade Kieron to eat more. However, when things still had not improved three or four months later, Sarah took him to the baby clinic to be checked over. She was concerned because Kieron seemed to have no energy – he certainly wasn't 'into everything' in the way that his older siblings had been at the same age – and was looking pale with dark circles around his eyes, despite still having quite a long sleep during the day. His language development was also a little behind that of his brothers and sister at the same age.

At the clinic it was discovered that Kieron's weight had dropped from the 50th to the 9th centile over a period of about six months. A developmental check revealed that Sarah had been right in thinking his language was delayed, and he was also a little behind in reaching some of the other milestones.

Sarah and the health visitor were puzzled by Kieron's situation. Sarah had already tried all of the suggestions the health visitor had made to try to encourage Kieron to eat – to no avail. The health visitor said that she would refer him to the paediatrician, and in the meantime Sarah should continue to do all she could to persuade Kieron to eat as much as possible.

Sarah was becoming more and more concerned that Kieron might have a serious illness, although she had not mentioned this at the clinic. The fact that the health visitor had not been able to get to the bottom of the problems just exacerbated her fears.

While they were waiting for the hospital appointment to come through, Richard and Sarah tried a variety of approaches with Kieron – feeding him alone, feeding him with the family or with other invited children, reducing the size of his helpings, offering him snacks between meals, not offering him snacks between meals, offering him his favourite foods. None of these tactics seemed to make any lasting difference and the parents' increasing anxiety began to affect their relationships with their other children. Sarah in particular realised that she was over-reacting to the other children's quite ordinary mealtime behaviours and that meals were becoming stressful for everyone.

They were pleased to receive the appointment to see the paediatrician quite quickly and were hopeful that she would provide them with some answers. Kieron was sent for several different medical tests, and as each came back negative, new tests were undertaken. Sarah was relieved that Kieron evidently did not have leukaemia but was still convinced that her little boy had a major illness.

Having had negative results to a range of increasingly invasive tests, the paediatrician finally declared herself satisfied that there was nothing medically wrong with Kieron. The health visitor was to be asked to monitor his progress and the parents should concentrate on increasing his food intake by whatever means they could.

Despite the extra attention received from the health visitor and the paediatrician, by the time Kieron reached his second birthday, his growth and development were still faltering. His parents remained anxious about his poor eating, and Sarah was still concerned that he might be seriously ill. His brothers and sisters were responding to the high levels of stress within the family and presenting increasingly demanding behaviours. Since she was monitoring his weight and progress, the health visitor was all too aware that things were not improving for Kieron and she too became increasingly anxious.

non-verbal mother–child interactions in unstructured home observations. In both groups, children's behavioural adjustment was linked to maternal negativity and cognitive performance was correlated with quality of stimulation. The authors concluded that developmental delay associated with chronic failure to thrive appeared more likely to arise from other influences, such as a previous biological insult, than to contemporaneous parenting practices.

Timing of FTT and catch-up growth

There is growing research evidence concerning sensitive or critical periods in terms of the impact of failure to thrive upon subsequent growth and development. For example, Skuse *et al.* (1992, 1994a, b) and Wolke (1996) have analysed data from their epidemiological study to compare children's growth depending upon age at onset of growth faltering. They conclude that the first few months appear to be a sensitive period for the relationship between growth and mental development:

> The prognosis of early [6 months or younger] failure to thrive is poor, both in terms of medium term growth and of cognitive development. It seems likely that there is a 'cumulative deficit' in terms of intellectual skills, with deteriorating performance between infancy and 4 years of age. (Skuse *et al.*, 1992, p. 66)

This conclusion was drawn on the basis of analysis of data on 49 subjects. Two families did not complete the assessment process. Of the 47 infants who were fully assessed, 22 showed onset before age 6 months and 25 had later onset. The authors reported that the early FTT onset infants in this study mainly explained the poor cognitive outcome they found in the index group (assessed with the Bayley Scales). On the other hand, no significant correlation was found between duration of growth retardation and mental outcome (Skuse *et al.*, 1994a).

Infants whose growth falters in postnatal life, who are socioeconomically disadvantaged and who are at high risk of inadequate parenting have been found to have 'contrasting outcomes depending upon whether that growth failure begins immediately after birth or later' (Skuse *et al.*, 1994b, p. S116). Children with onset after age 6 months were found to have mothers who were subject to greater adversity and might have been expected to provide relatively poor parenting. However, these children had better developmental outcomes in their second postnatal year than those with early onset FTT (who also had higher birth weights than the later onset children).

The significance of timing of onset of FTT in terms of outcomes is confirmed in clinical literature. Goodman (1994) summarises possible abnormalities in brain development at different stages. He concludes that environmental insults that affect the developing brain late in pregnancy and early in infancy may have their greatest impact on cerebella and hippocampal development, which in rats has been linked to hyperactivity and learning deficits.

Regarding the potential for catch-up growth and its benefits, Smart (1991) concludes: 'It proves to be very difficult to propose a useful general hypothesis on recovery from undernutrition because of the complex nature of brain development' (p. 119). However, it is generally recognised that, in view of the speed of brain growth in early childhood, in theory there is a strong case for early treatment of FTT (Wright, 1995).

POINTS FOR INTERVENTION

The discussion of the prevalence and effects of FTT suggests the following:

■ Since FTT can occur in any family, intervention strategies should be structured and provided in a non-stigmatising manner that is acceptable to all.

■ FTT interventions should be judged not only in terms of their success in re-establishing growth but also improving cognitive development, since there is the potential for this to be adversely affected by FTT.

■ Interventions should take account of differences between early onset (under 6 months of age) and late onset (6 months to 1 year of age) FTT in terms of effects and therefore treatment or intervention. Early onset is potentially more serious in terms of subsequent growth and development, so intervention should be speedy, especially for those who are socio-economically disadvantaged and who might be at risk of poor parenting because of high levels of adversity.

To summarise, the most important factors in FTT in terms of its effects are severity and timing of the episode, with early onset FTT potentially having the most serious long-term consequences for children. This seems to be more significant than the length of the FTT episode. These findings point to the importance of early identification of FTT with speedy application of appropriate intervention strategies. However, this needs to be set against the risk of catching too many 'false positives' in the net, since it is also known that infants and young children may display variations in their pattern of growth without failing to thrive. This highlights the importance of having well-established and clear-cut thresholds for identification of FTT, followed by staged interventions (described in Chapters 4 and 5).

Effects on carers, family and professionals

From the preceding discussion, it is clear that the effects of FTT have tended to be measured only in terms of children's growth and development. An important but often neglected area (illustrated in the earlier case study of Kieron and his family, pp. 24–5) is the effect FTT has upon the child's primary caregiver, other household or family members, and those health and social care professionals working with the family. This may be partly attributed to problems of measurement.

A child's weight or height can simply and accurately be recorded by means of scales or a measuring stick. How does one measure levels of distress and anxiety amongst parents of FTT children? How can one separate out the effects of FTT upon the family, and the effect that pre-existing family distress might have upon or contribute to the FTT? If we take an interactional model of FTT (as discussed in the next chapter) then a linear model of 'cause and effect' is too simplistic. Whilst at one level it is true to say that consumption of too few calories leads to poor growth, this is only part of the picture. The statement begs such questions as 'What preceded this FTT?' and 'What does poor growth lead to, in terms of distress for parents, other carers and professionals?' The next question might be 'How does this distress then affect the parents' ability to ensure that the child consumes adequate calories?'

Whatever factors initially contributed to a child consuming inadequate calories, Fig. 4 illustrates the process which might then result. If a child's rate of growth deteriorates it is likely to be identified in the first instance by

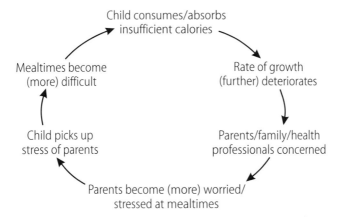

Fig. 4   Process of family interactions.

parents or other family members, or by health professionals in the context of a baby clinic. Most parents are distressed to learn that their child is not growing appropriately. A health professional expressing concern to parents about a child's poor growth, combined with advice on nutrition or feeding, might result in speedy resolution of the problem in one family but exacerbation of the problem in another, with mealtimes quickly becoming worrying and stressful occasions. Children are quick to pick up parental distress, so anxiety around feeding can quickly exacerbate any difficulties. This, in turn, puts the child at risk of consuming even fewer calories; so the cycle may go around again.

Such a process will affect everyone involved, as illustrated in Case Study 3 which describes the impact of Saul's FTT upon him and his family. Parents of FTT children often feel they are failing their child in some way; this can be exacerbated by the very label *failure* to thrive. When encouraged by health professionals to increase their child's level of food consumption they may, in desperation, resort to feeding practices which are distressing for them and for their child, such as forced feeding by nose holding. Being told that there is nothing medically wrong with their child may be reassuring on the one hand, but may also be experienced as a covert criticism of their parenting skills and abilities. If the child is subsequently hospitalised and gains weight, parents can experience this as a further undermining of their ability to raise their child successfully.

Case study 3
The impact of Saul's FTT on family dynamics

Saul had been difficult to feed from birth, and these difficulties were exacerbated when his parents tried to introduce solid foods into his diet at about 6 months of age. Other members of the family (grandparents and aunts) were no more successful in persuading him to eat. Medical investigations had revealed a minor problem, but this should not have affected Saul's feeding. The paediatrician impressed upon the parents the importance of increasing calorie intake and this added to their already high levels of anxiety.

At one of Saul's appointments with the paediatrician it was noted that his weight had fallen to the 0.4th centile (he had previously maintained a growth curve close to the 50th) and the decision was taken to supplement his calorie intake overnight with high calorie fluids via a naso-gastric tube. This provided a 'safety net' and prevented Saul's weight from dropping any further, but it meant that there was little incentive (hunger) to encourage him to take food orally for the early part of the day.

The family's efforts to enjoy mealtimes together were thwarted by the difficulties associated with feeding Saul. He started each meal sitting in a high chair, but when he consistently refused to eat, his parents would remove him to the settee where, in desperation, he was given most of his nourishment lying flat on his back. His mother tried spoon-feeding pureed foods and when this failed she used a plastic hypodermic syringe (minus the needle) to squirt the liquid food into the corner of his mouth. This was quickly washed down with drinks from a bottle. This process was distressing for everyone. Saul cried or screamed throughout, his mother was often tearful and always upset, and if other members of the family tried to feed him they also became unsettled and frustrated. Moreover, everyone was very concerned for Saul's older brother and the effect that all of this was having on him.

Saul had learned to expect that meals would be uncomfortable, distressing and full of anxiety and tension. He had no experiences of food as pleasurable or of mealtimes as comfortable social occasions. His parents and other carers also approached each meal with emotions running high and a sense of dread. The family felt unable to take holidays or even stay overnight with relatives because of the difficulties of feeding Saul, and extended family celebrations such as birthdays or weddings were a real ordeal.

From enjoying a reputation as an enthusiastic and adventurous cook, Saul's mother gradually lost all interest in the activities associated with food preparation. Apart from affecting the type of food provided for the family, this lowered her diminishing self-confidence still further. This in turn influenced her capacity to fulfil her role within her part-time job. Gradually Saul's mother had come to view her job as a means of gaining some respite from the torment of mealtimes with her youngest son. As her anxiety about him increased, however, her ability to concentrate on her work was affected.

The stresses and strains of coping with Saul's feeding difficulties also had a major impact on his parents' relationship. Almost the only topic of conversation between the couple was about how to do their best for Saul. Inevitably there were differences of opinion and this in turn increased the tension within the household.

By the time Saul reached his first birthday, every aspect of his family's life was affected by his feeding difficulties.

When a child's growth does not improve, health professionals may also feel they have failed the child. If standard advice about feeding is not successful in resolving the problem, health visitors may refer the child to a paediatrician via the GP. However, unless there is a well-developed model of assessment and intervention for FTT such as that described in Chapter 5 (pp. 82–9), the paediatrician's advice may be no more successful than that already provided through the baby clinic. Health visitors can then find the child discharged back to them, with the brief to monitor growth. They may then feel they are 'left holding the baby' with no prospect of effective intervention on offer (Batchelor and Kerslake, 1990). In Case Study 2 (pp. 24–5), the impact of Kieron's FTT upon the health visitor was evident.

The process illustrated in Fig. 4 starts with the child consuming inadequate calories for growth. However, this will in itself have been preceded by some event, set of circumstances or condition which resulted in the child first not eating sufficient food to meet their growth needs. One child might be a faddy or difficult feeder, rejecting lumpy food possibly as a result of minor oral-motor dysfunction. Such a child might be coaxed and encouraged to eat if parents have sufficient emotional and material resources. However, if the primary caregiver is distressed, depressed or overwhelmed for some reason (possibly unrelated to the child), they may not be sufficiently 'available' to meet that child's feeding needs. Another child might consume insufficient calories because parents lack knowledge about dietary needs. Very occasionally a child might not be given sufficient food because of overtly neglectful parents.

It may be useful to bear in mind the factors that may start the process of inadequate or faltering growth, as discussed here, when considering the causes of FTT in the next chapter.

SUMMARY

- Identification of FTT children in the past has been skewed by professionals' beliefs about FTT, particularly the perceived link between FTT and organic illness or neglect and abuse. Recent evidence suggests that only about 5 per cent of FTT children have a previously undiagnosed illness, and only a small minority are suffering from neglect or abuse.

- Comprehensive identification of all FTT children can only be achieved by weight monitoring or charting of all young children.

- Failure to thrive affects about 3 per cent of the infant population in developed countries.

- It occurs across all socio-economic groups, although rates vary across different ethnic groups.

- Families who are disadvantaged economically may face additional stresses and have fewer resources at their disposal, making their children potentially more vulnerable to FTT.

- Several studies have shown that FTT has an adverse effect on cognitive abilities as well as growth.

- The timing and severity of FTT, rather than its duration, are important in terms of effects, with onset before 6 months having more serious consequences than onset after 6 months.

■ Parental and/or professional concern over a child's weight faltering may start a cycle where increased anxiety over mealtimes/feeding exacerbates difficulties and leads to further weight loss.

3

CAUSAL FACTORS IN FTT

In an analysis of treatment or intervention methodologies it might be argued that what causes FTT is immaterial. The immediate task with any FTT child and their family is to resolve the FTT by addressing whatever is currently keeping it going. This will include tackling difficulties such as disrupted parent–child relationships, which may have arisen as a result of the FTT but which may now be contributing to it. However, it has already been established that there are many pathways to FTT and an understanding of those pathways is valuable in evaluating different interventions, in terms of their strengths and weaknesses. Understanding of aetiology is also important when looking at preventative strategies. The variety of factors that can contribute to a child's failure to thrive has increasingly been recognised by researchers and practitioners.

Organic *vs* non-organic

In recent years there have been many critiques of the traditional division of failure to thrive into organic or non-organic. Firstly, the proportion of children suffering from major organic conditions as the main cause of their failure to thrive appears to be very small: only 5 per cent of a screened population, according to Wright and Talbot (1996). Also, even where there is an underlying organic cause (ranging from coeliac disease and thyroid deficiency to asthma and oesophageal reflux), other non-organic factors may be operating.

Frank and Zeisel (1988) make the point that, whatever its origins, all children with failure to thrive will be suffering from an organic problem: 'All children with non-organic failure to thrive suffer from a serious organic insult: primary malnutrition' (p. 1187). So making a diagnostic distinction between organic and non-organic FTT may be irrelevant to treatment outcome. Bithoney *et al.* (1989) evaluated prospectively whether there was any difference in weight gain between non-organic and organic FTT children treated by a multidisciplinary team. They concluded that weight gain alone does not differentiate between the two. Benoit (1993) describes the consensus that 'the traditional etiologic dichotomy between organic and inorganic is misleading' (p. 62) (see also Douglas and Bryon, 1996).

Other studies warn that extensive physical testing of FTT children is likely to be unproductive. Frank and Zeisel (1988), in their overview of failure to thrive research and practice, observe:

> Unless an illness other than primary malnutrition is suggested by history or physical examination, the yield of extensive laboratory workup in children who fail to thrive is almost nil. (pp. 1193–4)

More recently, Marcovitch (1994), writing for the British medical profession, advises avoiding routine use of invasive medical techniques and being sensitive to the fact that hospital admission may only confound a situation.

As discussed in the previous chapters, early literature viewed non-organic FTT as arising from emotional deprivation, although this position has now been widely discredited. Many now take the view that non-organic FTT is due to inadequate intake of nutrition, whilst recognising that the routes to inadequate intake may be wide-ranging and result from a complex interaction of environmental and individual factors. Thus, within the discussion that follows, FTT will be taken to mean non-organic failure to thrive which may occur on its own, in conjunction with or as a result of organic FTT. The terms 'organic' and 'non-organic' will only be used if specified within the research cited.

Failure to thrive and abuse or neglect

Despite the mounting evidence from recent epidemiological and clinical studies that only a small minority of FTT children are also abused and neglected (Skuse *et al.*, 1994a; Wolke, 1996; Wright and Talbot, 1996), many practitioners and clinicians continue to locate FTT firmly in the domain of abuse and neglect. For example, one of the few recent papers on failure to thrive addressed at social workers focuses on emotional deprivation and stunted growth (Budd, 1990). Although Budd acknowledges that some doctors regard FTT as primarily a nutritional problem, she concludes (on the basis of two published studies) that emotionally abusing environments can cause growth problems in children. Recent work by Skuse has confirmed that a small number of children with an inborn constitutional predisposition will, in the face of stress or neglect, develop growth hormone deficiency which results in stunted growth. However, this is a very rare condition which affects perhaps three to five children per 10,000. The majority of poorly growing children are failing to thrive not because of emotional deprivation but because of undernutrition. Yet Budd's paper maintains a commonly held social work perspective on FTT: namely, that it is always the result of abuse or neglect. Whilst the potential for FTT occasionally to be the result of neglect must never be overlooked, such a perspective limits the likelihood of social workers developing FTT intervention strategies aimed at addressing much more common causal factors, such as feeding problems.

The common view in the social work profession that failure to thrive is synonymous with neglect or abuse was firmly established by FTT having been a category for registration of a child on a child protection register. Although such a category no longer exists, it is sustained by such publications as *Working Together under the Children Act 1989,* which included non-organic failure to thrive within the definition of neglect (Department of Health, 1991, p. 48). The ongoing but usually mistaken association made between failure to thrive and abuse or neglect in the minds of many social work professionals can be potentially obstructive. It can result in these professionals missing and hence not intervening with the majority of children who are failing to thrive, for the very reason that the majority are not the subject of abuse or neglect. On the other hand, for those families whose child is failing to thrive and who have some social work involvement, the 'abuse' label automatically attached by some to the FTT diagnosis may hinder constructive work with them.

Evidence for and against FTT as abuse or neglect

In the field of FTT research and practice, it is mainly social workers and clinicians who continue to place their work in the context of abuse and neglect. For example, Hanks *et al.* (1988) firmly categorise non-organic FTT, resulting from inadequate nutrition, as a form of child abuse. They suggest that the difficulty professionals face in accepting FTT as a form of abuse stems from the fact that the emotional and intellectual impact is not visible in the way physical injuries are. They suggest FTT is the result of failure to feed and, on the basis of their clinical experience, put this down to 'an antagonistic or chaotic emotional life of the parents and because of problems of interaction between mother and child' (p. 101). Such a conclusion has since been challenged by the findings of Skuse *et al.* (1992) and Wolke (1996) whose epidemiological studies have shown no significant differences between the mother–child interactions of FTT cases and controls (see p. 49). Hanks *et al.*'s position may be understandable in view of the fact that they draw only on clinical samples, where primary health care professionals have already screened, labelled and referred children as cases of FTT.

Yet the experience of many workers in this field is that the majority of parents of FTT children are struggling to get their child to consume more calories. This is illustrated in Case Study 4 of Juliette and her parents, Jane and Steven (pp. 41–2). Despite the fact that the endpoint is an undernourished child, many professionals would not consider such parents to be neglectful or abusive – quite the contrary. In subsequent writings Hanks and Hobbs (1993) quote Kempe and Kempe arguing that much failure to thrive was nutritional neglect resulting from feeding inadequate calories, either as a result of not enough food or a bizarre diet. This fails to take account of those households in which there is adequate, appropriate food made available to the child but because of major feeding difficulties they are not consumed, despite caregivers' best efforts. Although it has been found that early post-natal FTT may be a risk factor for later serious parenting deficiencies which may warrant professional intervention (Skuse *et al.*, 1995), more than eight out of ten cases give no further cause for concern.

Other workers in the FTT field hold views which differ from those of Hanks and her colleagues. Drotar (1988) makes some useful observations about FTT and abuse or neglect. He writes, 'Environmentally based FTT is often erroneously equated with neglect and, in some states [in the USA], is a legally accepted criterion of neglect' (Drotar, 1988, p. 85). However, he does acknowledge that a child ingesting too few calories for their growth needs could, strictly speaking, be considered neglected. This raises the questions, What is meant by abuse? By neglect? Does abuse necessarily mean abusive *intent* was present? (O'Hagan, 1993).

Stevenson (1995) discusses the notion of parental culpability in child neglect and the importance of properly assessing parental failure in such cases. She distinguishes between maltreatment and 'harm'; it is possible for a child to be harmed without intentional maltreatment. However, most neglect cases with which social workers become involved have both. In addition, neglect often results in injury or (in the case of FTT) in permanent developmental delay and cognitive impairment. Stevenson discusses the British 'neglect of neglect', as do Minty and Patterson (1994). They define neglect as:

> persistent failure to meet a child's essential needs by omitting basic parenting tasks and responsibilities ... in spite of parents having the economic resources to meet these needs at a basic level. (p. 736)

Schmitt and Mauro (1989), reviewing their clinical experience and the research literature on outpatient treatment of FTT, suggest that non-organic FTT can be accidental, neglectful (mild or extreme) or deliberate. They conclude that accidental or mild neglectful FTT can be managed by outpatient work whereas extreme neglect or deliberate FTT (by withholding of food) may require a higher level of intervention, such as removal of children to foster care. Similarly, Wright and Talbot (1996) differentiate between neglect as wilful omission and emotional abuse as acts of commission. They make explicit the steps they take in resolving FTT before it can be attributed to abuse or neglect.

In conclusion, it is generally inaccurate to locate FTT within the abuse and neglect spectrum. As Drotar (1988) wrote in his review of FTT, 'the coincidence of FTT and abuse is infrequent'. Marcovitch (1994) stresses the importance of not assuming that if a poorly growing child comes from a materially or emotionally deprived background s/he is necessarily neglected. However, failure to thrive and neglect will coincide for a few children (Wright and Talbot, 1996). Wolke (1996) suggests a very small subgroup (but mostly seen at clinics) are actually neglected or deprived leading to FTT; this conclusion is based on a large-scale community-based prospective study. Likewise Wright (1995), reporting on the first 50 FTT cases found using the Thrive Index (see p. 7) as a screening tool, noted that overt neglect was comparatively rare. Powell and Reid (1994), in their team work with 20 children referred by paediatricians for FTT, found only one case that involved child protection issues.

Effect of FTT and neglect

Whilst neglect may only rarely be associated with failure to thrive, there is evidence to suggest that when they are both present, the long-term effects are considerable. Mackner *et al.* (1997) used a cumulative risk model to examine the relationship between neglect, FTT and cognitive functioning in low income children in the USA. They concluded that the cognitive performance of children suffering from both neglect and FTT was significantly below that of children suffering from only neglect or only FTT. However, it should be borne in mind that Mackner *et al.* used the Caldwell and Bradley (1984) HOME scales or inventories to define neglect. These scales measure the quality of stimulation and support available to a child at home, but are not unproblematic. For example, Bradley (1993) notes that it is unclear whether they precisely capture differences in environmental quality in all cultures. Despite these limitations, it is evident that when FTT and abuse or neglect do co-exist it is 'indicative of extraordinary risk to the child' (Drotar, 1988).

An interactional perspective on FTT

The FTT literature reflects both the multifactorial aetiology of FTT and an increasing awareness of the value of an interactional perspective. For example, Benoit (1993) summarises research findings which describe phenomenological aspects of FTT, under characteristics of FTT infants (e.g. nutritional, developmental, emotional and behavioural); of their mothers (e.g. psychopathology); of the caregiver–infant relationship; and of the family. Similarly Williams (1994), writing from her clinical experience as a paediatric dietitian (and addressing those in clinical practice), summarises causes of non-organic FTT as child-based, such as mechanical feeding difficulties, delayed feeding skills or food refusal; carer-based, such as provision of inappropriate feed type/volume, dietary misconceptions or ignorance; or based on wider environmental factors such as poverty.

Some researchers and practitioners have gone on to develop or propose models for assessment and intervention which explicitly take account of the interactional nature of FTT. For example, Reifsnider (1995), writing for public health nurses, suggests the 'Eco–Epi' (ecological–epidemiological) model to provide a framework for planning interventions with FTT children and their families. This comprises an examination of the epidemiological concepts of agent (food), host (child) and environment (home), in the ecological context of the microsystem (parent–child interaction, daily activities of the family), the mesosystem (interactions between different environments) and the exosystem (the child's community). (For a study using a similar model, see Lobo *et al.* (1992) based on Barnard and Eyres (1979).)

Psychological, behavioural and interactional factors all come into play in the arena of feeding (e.g. Douglas and Bryon, 1996; Skuse, 1993). Feeding difficulties may both be caused by an interplay of different factors and also set off problems in interactive processes. In terms of causes, Williams (1994) suggests that factors to be considered when assessing causes of feeding problems should include feeding behaviour and non-feeding interactions, social background and temperament of the child as well as dietary history and growth. In terms of effects of feeding problems, Ramsay (1995) writes:

> the reaction to physiologically or medically based feeding disturbances may give rise to interactional and psychological problems, which in turn may exacerbate maladaptive behaviors and the original feeding problem. (p. 609)

A brief description of the two major factors significant in an interactional model of FTT follows, although it is apparent that neither can be seen in isolation from the other and both may include environmental factors. For example, a child may be temperamentally difficult and predisposed to feeding problems and their primary carer may have a personal history of having been abused, resulting in low self-esteem and lack of confidence in parenting. These two factors alone might result in the child's intake of calories being inadequate for growth, as feeding becomes a stressful and unproductive activity. Additionally, for some families there may be further factors related to the environment; for example, high levels of deprivation may mean a family lacks basic facilities (such as a table at which to eat), exacerbating difficulties at mealtimes. It is evident that, individually or in combination, these factors can lead to major problems of diet and nutritional deficiencies (e.g. iron deficiency, Harris and Booth, 1992; anaemia, Williams, 1994; undernutrition, Wright, 1995).

Child factors in FTT

Children predisposed to FTT

Skuse (1993) and Wolke (1996) suggest, from epidemiological work, that certain sub-groups of children are at risk of FTT. Some appear to have little appetite, do not demand feeds and are prone to sleep through the night from an early age, as illustrated in Case Study 4 of Juliette. If not woken for feeds such children may then learn to go for long periods without food so reprogramming their appetite regulation system. Similarly children with subtle oral-motor problems (some of whom may become food refusers) may be exclusively breast-fed beyond the point when breast milk is sufficient for their growth needs. There may also be infants who fail to thrive at the breast as they are restless, cry excessively or do not latch onto the nipple, and so do not complete feeds (Skuse, 1993).

Case study 4
Child and family factors resulting in failure to thrive

In common with many expectant parents, Jane and Steven had talked about the things they would do in order to give their baby the best start in life. That they would love him or her unreservedly was without question, and it was important to Jane and Steven that their child should have every opportunity to reach his or her potential.

They read all they could about pregnancy, childbirth and the early years of child development and by the time Juliette was born they felt well prepared.

From the start Juliette was a 'good' baby, feeding quite well and sleeping for long periods between feeds. In fact she often fell asleep whilst still at the breast and of all the babies born recently amongst Jane's circle of friends was the first to sleep through the night. Jane was enjoying her time at home with the baby, although things had turned out somewhat differently than she had anticipated. She had expected to be spending much more time playing with Juliette, but all her friends told her how lucky she was that she had such a good baby. Jane suppressed her faint sense of disappointment about the way her relationship with Juliette was developing.

When it was time to introduce her to solids, Jane and Steven carried out their plan to ensure that Juliette had as healthy a diet as possible. They offered her freshly prepared foods and ensured that no sugar or salt was added. She did not seem to like many of the new tastes and Jane and Steven struggled to find things that she would eat. Despite the fact that she was still receiving breast milk, Juliette's weight began to falter. By the time she was 10 months old she had fallen from the 50th centile for weight to the 9th and Jane and Steven had become increasingly anxious about her. Their vision of sociable and enjoyable family mealtimes had vanished in the face of the stressful and distressing reality.

When they were asked to keep a food diary recording everything that Juliette ate in a week, this highlighted for Jane and Steven that although she refused many of the foods they offered her, there were some things that she always ate. However, because these foods were quite high in fat and sugar, they did not fit comfortably with their view of what constituted a good healthy diet for an infant. The estimated calorie content of Juliette's food intake revealed that she needed considerably more calories per day to maintain her existing centile position for weight. It was unlikely that she would get these from decreasing breast-feeds.

Jane and Steven struggled with the advice that they should offer, more often, the foods that Juliette was known to like and eat, in order to increase her calorific intake. This information represented a real challenge to their understanding and belief about what constituted a healthy diet and they spent many hours talking about what they should do for the best. In the meantime the difficulties in persuading Juliette to eat were continuing – and if anything getting worse.

This situation represented a real crisis for Jane and Steven – they could not agree on what was best for their child and each began to blame the other for the difficulties. Steven felt that it was vital that Juliette should be able to enjoy any food that she would eat and that there was time to worry about a healthy diet later on. Jane took the longer-term view and was anxious that Juliette should eat the right foods in order to have a healthy adult life.

An infant's level of responsiveness is a significant factor in parent–child interactions. Some FTT children may express less positive affect in feeding and non-feeding situations (Polan *et al.*, 1991), possibly as a result of acute or chronic malnutrition. An unresponsive child will influence the way a parent responds when attempting to feed them, thus potentially further contributing to a pattern of poor food intake.

In addition, infant developmental status has been found to be closely related to interactional style (Wolke, 1996). The lower the developmental status of infants (regardless of whether they were FTT cases or matched controls), the less appropriate and sensitive were the interactions observed between mother and infant. Some infants communicate their needs (including need for food) unequivocally whilst others, including FTT infants, are poorer in their non-verbal communication. Skuse *et al.* (1992) note factors associated with FTT include the 'infant's lack of competence in communicating clearly and unambiguously their needs during mealtimes' (pp. 66–7).

Feeding skills disorders and oral-motor problems

Feeding difficulties in children constitute an important group of causal factors in FTT. Ramsay, whose studies on FTT preschool children are described below (p. 44), has estimated that between 50 and 70 per cent of children with FTT have a history of feeding difficulties (Ramsay, personal communication). This figure is based on clinical samples; however, epidemiological work also supports an association between feeding difficulties and failure to thrive.

Many authors stress that feeding difficulties may arise from and be sustained by a combination of factors. Harris and Booth (1992), on the basis of extensive clinical experience in the UK, conclude that chronic feeding problems often arise from a combination of early predisposing factors (e.g. in the child, carer or environment) and subsequent mismanagement of the process of feeding. Similarly Skuse (1993), addressing practitioners and drawing on a range of studies of feeding problems, notes the range of causal factors. They may include low-grade oral-motor dysfunction, communication difficulties that inhibit requests for food (confirmed by Lindberg *et al.*, 1996), lack of self-feeding skills and parental psychopathology. He notes that 'growth failure may occur as a consequence of a ... subtle interaction between infant characteristics and parental response' (p. 607).

The research described below is divided into feeding skills disorders and oral-motor problems although there may be considerable overlap in the difficulties they encompass.

Feeding skills disorders

A particular group of infant or child factors which may predispose some children to FTT is feeding skills disorders. Several studies have highlighted the importance of feeding skills (or lack of them) in FTT. For example, Ramsay *et al.* (1993) report on their study, undertaken in Canada, of preschool FTT children referred to their multidisciplinary Failure to Thrive and Eating Disorders Clinic. They found that feeding problems started early with non-organic FTT infants, with symptoms starting within the first few months after birth and similar in nature to those exhibited by some of the infants with organic FFT. This led Ramsay *et al.* (1993) to conclude that they all suffered from feeding skills disorders. They state:

> Difficulties during the early stages of feeding development may not only interfere with the development of more mature feeding skills, but also may contribute towards later behavioural and interactional problems between mothers and infants. (Ramsay *et al.*, 1993, p. 294)

In summary, they conclude that early feeding impairment may trigger the development of maladaptive interactional patterns between some infants and their mothers, whilst other mothers may be successful in compensating for their infants' inefficient feeding (see Compensatory parenting, pp. 48-9). In a review of the literature, Ramsay *et al.* also suggest that the use of the term non-organic FTT for inadequate food intake may need to be reconsidered, perhaps shifting the focus from maternal characteristics to characteristics of infant feeding as possible causal factors.

Oral-motor problems

Skuse *et al.* (1994a) and Wolke (1996) suggest, on the basis of their prospective epidemiological study in the UK aimed at identifying the origins of FTT, that subtle oral-motor problems are a risk factor and early oral-motor functioning should be a focus of assessment. Wilensky *et al.* (1996), in his study in Israel, found the average length of each breast-feed was longer for their FTT group (19.5 minutes) than for matched controls (12.9 minutes) and the difference was statistically significant ($p<0.05$). This may be supporting evidence for those FTT children having mild oral-motor dysfunction from the outset, which meant they were slow feeders even at the breast. As they state:

> Although we did not examine oromotor function directly, the failure to thrive infants did take longer to finish each breast feed. Thus there may be some indirect evidence for the presence of mild oromotor difficulties in the failure to thrive infants, as reported by Skuse *et al.* (Wilensky *et al.*, 1996, p. 147)

Reilly (1997) has since estimated that oral-motor dysfunction is a factor for 25 per cent of FTT infants.

Oral-motor functioning was the focus of work by Mathisen *et al.* (1989). They built on earlier work (Heptinstall *et al.*, 1987) in which it had been found that 11 out of 23 study children aged 4 with poor growth living in socio-emotionally disadvantaged families displayed oral incoordination when feeding. Hence Mathisen *et al.* (1989) went on to develop a Feeding Assessment Schedule to quantify oral-motor functioning and used it to investigate the prevalence of such dysfunctions amongst a sample of FTT children. They pair-matched nine non-organic FTT infants with comparison infants and found some evidence that the study infants performed less well than the comparison infants on a range of indices of oral-motor functioning and feeding skills. Study children were less adept than comparisons in communicating their needs at mealtimes (also reported by Skuse *et al.* (1992) in their epidemiological studies). They also noted that several of the study children (mean age almost 1 year) seemed 'hypersensitive to tactile stimuli, especially in the oral region' (p. 298) and suggested a possible circular effect arising from this hypersensitivity; that is, they suggest an interactional perspective. If tensions already exist between a mother and child around feeding, a child's oral hypersensitivity may predispose them to an adverse response to their mother's touch. This might then be understood by her as a sign of rejection, resulting in feeding becoming a purely functional rather than a social activity (as was observed in Mathisen *et al.*'s study).

However, it should be noted that these study infants were already growing poorly, and seven of the nine had previously been referred to hospital for investigation of their poor growth. Their sensitivity to touch around the mouth may have arisen from earlier negative feeding experiences (e.g. food that was too hot; bruising with a spoon; naso-gastric feeding when hospitalised) which then resulted in both their sensitivity to touch and a reduced intake of nutrition, leading to poor growth. Mathisen *et al.* (1989) conclude that important factors in FTT are contextual (e.g. location of feeding, positioning of child), child attributes (e.g. hypersensitivity to touch) and maladaptive interactional features (e.g. children not being good at communicating their needs at mealtimes). For some children this may then be compounded by having mothers whose mealtimes lack organisation or who cannot respond sensitively to the problem (Heptinstall *et al.*, 1987). If these mothers are, for whatever reason, unable to provide appropriate compensatory parenting (Ramsay, 1995; see p. 48 below), poor growth may result from the child not consuming sufficient food, despite it having been made available to them.

More recently, Douglas and Bryon (1996) have obtained data (by means of semi-structured diagnostic interviews) from parents of 201 children under 7 with severe behavioural feeding difficulties, to aid classification and understanding of children referred to their hospital-based psychological treatment programme. Children were assessed from the interview data by assistant psychologists or clinical staff, but no reliability measures were obtained. No control group was used, although some comparisons were made with findings from various population studies of young children and eating. Oral-motor difficulties were assessed indirectly by means of identification of speech delay. Nineteen per cent of sample children showed mild delay and 10 per cent severe delay, which Douglas and Bryon report is high compared to the normal population. The proportion of parents reporting mild behaviour problems with their children was also higher amongst cases than estimates in an urban population, although parent reports were not verified by scores on behaviour checklists. Most noteworthy was the finding that many children first showed feeding difficulties at a very early age and frequent and long-lasting vomiting was common in the first year of life, during which time avoidance learning seems to have become well established.

Mother/carer factors in FTT

Parenting and parent–child interactions

Early FTT research concluded that maternal deprivation was a major factor in FTT. In recent years this view has been steadily discredited, as more sophisticated and methodologically sound research has been undertaken (see Recent evidence on mother–infant interactions, p. 49). However, there continues to be an emphasis on the role of mothers in FTT. Few researchers address broader parenting issues and their relevance to FTT aetiology, or the role of fathers and family functioning in general (Drotar, 1991).

Boddy and Skuse (1994) undertook an extensive review of the literature on parenting of children with FTT to determine both the extent of the evidence that there are differences between parents of thriving children and those who fail to grow, and to pose questions about the direction of future research. They conclude there may be an association between parenting behaviour and infant growth retardation but suggest 'there has yet to be an adequate explanation of parental thinking' (Boddy and Skuse, 1994, p. 419), by which they mean the way parents think about their child, and their perceptions of and responses to him or her. They attribute this lack of understanding of the role of parental cognition to the theoretical weakness of many studies and their failure to attend to developments in psychology, particularly the study of social cognition.

Some earlier work had already attempted to encompass such issues. For example, Drotar et al. (1990) compared interactional behaviour of mothers and FTT infants who had been hospitalised with that of mothers and matched physically healthy infants. They observed mothers of FTT infants to have less adaptive social interactional behaviour but also acknowledged the need for further studies to clarify the direction of influence between maternal and child behaviour. It should also be remembered that these children had been hospitalised, which in itself is likely to have affected mother–child interactions. Ward et al. (1993) found disrupted parent–child relationships and stressful social environments to be common in FTT but acknowledged the part malnourished FTT children may play in the aetiology of their disorder. As they state:

It is likely that anxious attachments in children with FTT arise from a complex transaction among characteristics of the child, characteristics of the mother, and characteristics of the social environment … the high frequency of anxious attachments among children with FTT may reflect the disruptive effects of a child's serious illness (especially malnutrition) on infant–parent interaction and the resulting attachments. (Ward *et al.*, 1993, p. 219)

Compensatory parenting

An important dimension in parent–child interactions is the ability of the parent to compensate for any difficulties a child has in feeding. The issue of compensatory parenting was indirectly addressed by Skuse *et al.* (1992) in their analysis of findings from their first epidemiological study. They found that case infants showed signs of neurological immaturity or dysfunction in gross motor and oral-motor skills and concluded:

When these characteristics are present, *and the caretaker does not recognize and adapt to the infant's special needs and vulnerabilities,* our observations suggest the growth problem may be exacerbated by chronic undernutrition, not because of inadequate provision of food but because of impaired ingestion. (p. 67, my italics)

In other words, they recognised that children with such special needs may have caretakers who can compensate by acknowledging those circumstances and then adapting their feeding to overcome difficulties and ensure adequate intake of food.

Ramsay (1995) has since written further about maternal compensatory feeding practices, this time in the context of various critiques of the definition of a feeding disorder (FD) in the *Diagnostic and Statistical Manual* (DSM-IV) (American Psychiatric Association, 1994). She writes:

DSM-IV states that the essential feature of FD is persistent failure to eat adequately, as reflected in 'significant failure to gain weight or loss of weight'. Such a statement does not take into account compensatory maternal efforts at feeding their infants who have intrinsic feeding difficulties, to avoid weight loss. (Ramsay, 1995, p. 607)

She suggests that weight gain is not solely an index of feeding ability but also of maternal compensatory feeding practices, and her clinical experiences point to the likelihood that the more severe the intrinsic feeding difficulties (such as undiagnosed oral-motor dysfunction) and the harder mothers work at compensating for such problems without success, the greater the likelihood of interactional difficulties arising. On the basis of a study of neonatal and later sucking ability, she also concludes that even amongst healthy infants there may be more with problematic feeding abilities than have previously been recognised (Ramsay and Gisel, 1996).

Recent evidence on mother–infant attachments

The work of Skuse, Wolke and Reilly, through analysis of their two large-scale epidemiological studies, has challenged earlier views regarding mother–infant attachments. For example Skuse *et al.* (1992) and more recently Wolke (1996), reporting on their 1986 birth cohort survey, found no differences in either temperament or attachment behaviour between cases and comparisons. They had hypothesised that family functioning and mother–infant interaction would be poorer in non-organic FFT families than in comparison families. Their findings did not support their hypotheses: they found no differences in psychiatric disorders of parents, maternal depression or marital problems in the two groups. Assessment of mother–toddler interaction during feeds and play was undertaken (and rated by raters blind to case/comparison status) but no significant differences in maternal, infant or joint behaviour were found.

Both Skuse and Wolke conclude from their epidemiological studies that there is little evidence of maternal deprivation (or of neglect or abuse) amongst non-organic FTT families, in contrast to the experiences of clinicians in this field. However, they do report that maternal IQ strongly determined 'interactional synchrony'; that is, the lower the IQ of mothers, the poorer were mother–child interactions. Such mothers were perhaps also limited in the extent to which they might provide compensatory parenting to infants who were predisposed to feeding difficulties, as discussed above.

Boddy (1997) has since reported on a study following up some mothers of FTT children identified in the epidemiological studies conducted by Skuse *et al.* (1994b). She examined whether timing of growth failure in the first year was related to maternal problem-solving strategies at 6 years. Her findings indicated that the child's development subsequent to growth faltering partly corresponds to the mother's problem-solving (Boddy, 1997), although she highlighted the need for prospective research to determine the causal nature of the associations found.

Feeding practices at weaning

A number of studies have looked at caregivers' feeding practices with infants at the stage of weaning and have highlighted the narrow 'window' when they might successfully introduce infants to solids, with delayed introduction of solids or new textures sometimes leading to food refusal (Blissett, 1997). Wolke (1994), in a summary of normative trends in eating, states:

> The basic oral-motor movement patterns for solid feeding are dependent on maturation but the acceptance of lumpy food and the associated mouth opening, lip movements, munching and swallowing patterns appear to involve practice and experience with such food. (p. 537)

The 'unexplained' variations in rates of FTT across various ethnic groups noted by Skuse et al. (1992) may be explained by an understanding of different traditions regarding feeding of young children, some of which may better fit with this 'window' and allow for subsequent practice than others. From contacts with current practitioners, it is apparent that delayed weaning is regarded as a factor in missing the window of opportunity but views about its culturally specificity were divided. However, one dietitian observed, on the basis of her clinical work, that Asian mothers chose not to use high chairs, preferring to feed children on their knee. This made moves to independent feeding difficult although it may have had other positive benefits.

A possible further complication of weaning may be a lack of nutrients in home-prepared weaning foods. Stordy et al. (1995) found many food samples in their study were low in energy, protein, fat, iron, calcium and zinc and some have identified excessive consumption of fruit juice as a contributing factor to FTT (Smith and Lifshitz, 1994). Two practitioners contacted for this review (both dietitians) spontaneously raised the issue of high fluid intake as a contributory factor in FTT for some children, reducing their appetite and sometimes resulting in anaemia.

Eating attitudes and habits of mothers

Another area of study has been the effect of eating attitudes of mothers with children with feeding disorders, some of whom may fit definitions of FTT. McCann *et al.* (1994) studied eating habits and attitudes concerning body shape and weight among 26 mothers of children with non-organic FTT (the index group). The children, aged 1–9½, were identified from referrals from GPs to paediatricians for FTT, and had a weight at or below the 3rd centile at referral. The index mothers' attitudes and habits were compared with equivalent data on individually matched women who participated in a large community survey (the comparison group). The authors report that mothers of non-organic FTT children had higher levels of dietary restraint compared to the comparison group. Despite their children's low weight, half of the index mothers restricted their child's intake of 'sweet' foods and a third restricted foods they considered 'fattening' or 'unhealthy', although no figures are given for the comparison group. McCann *et al.* conclude that careful inquiry about the mothers' eating habits and attitudes should form part of the assessment of FTT children.

Stein *et al.* (1994) conducted an observational study of an index group of 34 mothers with eating disorders (DSM-III-R diagnosis), and a comparison group of 24 matched control women; all had children aged 12–24 months. Mother–child interaction at home was videotaped and rated by raters who were blind to the mothers' group membership. The mothers in the index group were found to be less facilitating during play and exhibited more conflict with their children during mealtimes and play, although positive expressed emotion was the same for the two groups. Index infants were rated as less happy during mealtimes and play. They also tended to be lighter than infants in the comparison group, despite the fact that their birth weights were very similar. The extent of mother–infant conflict during mealtimes and degree of the mother's concerns about her own body shape were both inversely related to infant weight. The authors note the limitations of the study (e.g. small number of subjects) and stress that on a number of outcome measures there was considerable variability within the index group. However, they conclude that their findings provide evidence of an association between eating disorders in women and disturbances in parenting, mother–infant interaction and infant development at one year.

POINTS FOR INTERVENTION

The discussion of causal factors in FTT in this chapter suggests the following regarding interventions:

■ Differentiating FTT children into organic and non-organic is of limited value.

■ There is no case for routinely undertaking extensive, invasive laboratory tests with FTT children.

■ Failure to thrive is rarely associated with abuse or neglect; any intervention should *not* start from an assumption that a child who is failing to thrive is neglected.

■ Models of assessment and intervention should take account of the multifactorial aetiology of FTT, and address factors in the child, carer, wider family and environment.

■ Child factors to be addressed should include predisposition to feed inefficiently, feeding skills disorders, oral-motor problems, and developmental status.

■ Carer factors to be addressed should include their capacity to provide compensatory parenting, their own eating habits and attitudes to food, and any history of having been abused in their childhood.

Stein *et al.* (1995) have since studied eating habits and attitudes of mothers with children with feeding difficulties and conclude that there is an association between the two. Mothers of children with a feeding problem showed significant disturbance in eating habits and attitudes whereas mothers of behaviourally disturbed children (the comparison group) were not different from the community controls. They suggest that when children have feeding problems, parents should be asked (carefully and sensitively) about their own eating habits and attitudes. Similarly Douglas and Bryon (1996) suggest maternal eating attitudes may be a significant factor amongst young children with severe behavioural eating difficulties.

Russell *et al.* (1998) studied a small group of mothers who were anorexic and found that of the 14 children in the group, nine had suffered food deprivation which the authors conclude stemmed from their anorexic mothers' abnormal concerns with body size. It should also be borne in mind that Wolke (1996) states, on the basis of analysis of epidemiological studies, that a small subgroup of overweight mothers may practise vicarious dieting with their infants.

The mental health of carers

Douglas (1991), writing for health visitors about the work of the Great Ormond Street Day Centre treatment programme, draws attention to the impact that feeding problems can have on the carer's mental health. Skuse *et al.* (1994b) also found a relationship between FTT and depression amongst mothers: namely, mothers of children with early onset FTT had levels of depression comparable with most pregnant women whilst those whose children had late onset FTT showed significantly higher levels of depression (on the basis of the General Health Questionnaire). Mothers of late onset FTT children were subject to greater levels of social and pyschological adversity.

Concerns about levels of depression amongst mothers of FTT children are also evident from contacts with current practitioners. One member of a feeding/FTT team reported that some mothers referred to the team were depressed but unable to afford the cost of a prescription for anti-depressants. The team member considered this hindered effective work with parents to overcome the FTT. One research project is underway in North Staffordshire examining possible links between postnatal depression and FTT.

Maternal history of abuse

The experience of mothers in terms of physical or sexual abuse in their own childhood has been addressed, sometimes indirectly, in a few studies. Archer and Szatmari (1990) report on a single case study of a mother who had been sexually and physically abused in childhood, including having experienced punishment for not eating (see p. 68). Weston and Colloton (1993) studied 59 mothers of children under 5 referred for non-organic FTT and a comparison group of 131 mothers of children with normal growth. Mothers were only included in the study if they had no recorded history of abuse and no history of treatment for emotional or psychiatric problems. The authors report that 80 per cent of the non-organic FTT mothers stated they were victims of abuse and they had a significantly higher level of history of abuse than the comparison group ($p<0.001$). Weston and Colloton suggest it is important to question mothers of FTT children regarding their own experiences of abuse; if they have a history of abuse the focus of treatment should then be on the mother–child dyad.

Conclusion

In conclusion, major causal factors in FTT, identified in the literature, can be grouped broadly into one of two areas: individual factors relating to the infant or child and individual factors relating to the primary caregiver. Each group of factors can encompass biological, social and psychological dimensions. Any or all of these factors may have a direct impact upon children, rendering some at risk of FTT. However, as has been touched upon in the preceding discussion, these factors converge at the point of infant–carer interaction, often in very subtle yet important ways (Skuse, 1993), particularly in the arena of mealtimes, feeding and eating. These factors must also be considered in the context of wider family, social and environmental factors. Some families may experience highly stressful environmental factors and infant or child factors which put them at high risk of FTT (Drotar, 1991), but because the child receives good compensatory care (Ramsay, 1995) from their primary carer, potential feeding difficulties are avoided or overcome and they eat well enough for growth. For other families, negative environmental factors such as deprivation, disadvantage and poverty will be the final straw in 'tipping' a child already predisposed to feeding problems (for example, because of low level oral-motor dysfunction) into an FTT episode.

SUMMARY

- The traditional division of FTT into organic and non-organic has limited value, as all children with FTT will be suffering from malnutrition. Only around 5 per cent of children have a major organic condition as the main cause of their failure to thrive.

- It is erroneous to assume that FTT is always the result of neglect or abuse. In the small proportion of cases where neglect and FTT do coincide, though, the effects can be severe.

■ An interactional perspective on the causes of FTT has gained increasing currency over recent years. Within this, the major causal factors can be grouped into those relating to (a) the child and (b) the caregiver. Interactions between these factors may be further affected by environmental factors, such as economic disadvantage.

■ Major child factors comprise feeding skills disorders and oral-motor dysfunctions.

■ Recent studies have challenged the view that maternal deprivation is a major cause of FTT: they found no differences in family functioning or mother–infant interactions in FTT families compared to controls.

■ Some caregivers may be able to compensate for their child's feeding problems by recognising the difficulties and adapting their feeding accordingly.

■ There is evidence of an association between mothers' eating disorders and children with feeding difficulties.

■ Failure to thrive in a child can affect the mental health of the caregiver.

4

INTERVENTIONS FOR FTT AND FEEDING PROBLEMS
WHAT WORKS?

In this chapter, findings from a broad spectrum of failure to thrive and feeding disorders intervention studies published between 1988 and 1998 are reviewed (see Appendix for details). Some are simply descriptions of management approaches, whilst a few are randomised controlled trials which provide important objective evidence of effectiveness.

Findings from these published studies have been supplemented by information from two sources. Firstly, the findings from a number of published summaries of clinical practice or reviews of research in this field are cited. They provide useful overviews of effective interventions, although criteria by which effectiveness is judged are not always given. Secondly, data gathered by means of the author's contacts with current practitioners have been used to supplement the discussion, although very few of these practitioners had undertaken any form of evaluation or outcome study to assess the effectiveness of their interventions.

The preceding chapter on causal factors in FTT makes it clear that children who suffer from FTT are not a homogeneous group with a common aetiology. Various factors, alone or in combination, will be responsible for each child's FTT. Therefore assessment and intervention programmes need to be flexible if they are to meet the needs of the majority of FTT children. Much literature on resolution or treatment addresses the assessment stage, recognising its crucial role in designing effective intervention. At its best, assessment is part of the overall intervention process rather than a discrete stage in its own right. For this reason, in the following summary of treatment models and intervention strategies, assessment procedures are also described whenever known.

Preliminary notes on the intervention studies

Before reviewing the studies of interventions, there are two topics – both discussed in Chapter 3 – which need to be borne in mind when looking at the research findings. The first is abuse or neglect; the second is the division of FTT into organic or non-organic.

Failure to thrive and abuse or neglect

It is interesting that some researchers, generally clinicians, continue to address FTT from the perspective of abuse and neglect, despite the low co-incidence between FTT and child abuse (Drotar, 1988). As discussed in the preceding chapter, more recent epidemiological studies confirm that there is little evidence of abuse or neglect amongst FTT families (Skuse *et al.*, 1995; Wolke, 1996). Presumably some practitioners continue to link FTT and neglect or abuse because such children comprise a significant proportion of those FTT children with whom they come into contact in their clinical work (although they comprise only a small proportion of the FTT population). This perspective may in part be perpetuated by the use of 'failure to thrive' as an indicator of abuse and neglect in much of the social work literature. This position is compounded by the fact that one very specific form of FTT known as psychosocial dwarfism is thought to be caused by extreme emotional abuse and rejection in early childhood.

However, those children who are failing to thrive and are abused or neglected will have experienced some of the same causal or contributory factors as other FTT children. At the very least they will share the common experience of inadequate intake of calories. Thus research on this subgroup of FTT children will still have some relevance to the full spectrum of children failing to thrive, and is therefore incorporated in the following discussion.

Organic *vs* non-organic: Is this distinction meaningful?

Many writers in this field have made the point that the categorisation of FTT as either organic or non-organic is of limited value. As discussed in Chapter 3, all FTT will occur as a result of undernutrition. Where there is an under-lying organic cause (such as a previously undiagnosed illness) this does not preclude the possibility that there are also non-organic factors operating. The two conditions are not mutually exclusive and there is evidence that all children who have FTT – regardless of aetiology – have either not taken, not been offered or not retained adequate calories to meet their requirements. As cited in Chapter 3, Bithoney *et al.* (1989) set out to test whether organic and non-organic FTT children would grow at similar rates when treatment was by provision of psychosocial support, medical care and high calorie diets. They report on an outpatient trial of a multidisciplinary team intervention strategy in Boston, USA; their sample was drawn from referrals to their FTT outpatient clinic. Children in both the organic FTT group and the non-organic FTT group grew well. The majority of studies cited below do not differentiate between organic and non-organic FTT and Bithoney *et al.*'s findings support this position.

Overviews and summaries of FTT research and clinical practice

Starting with overviews of FTT research and clinical practice published in the late 1980s, Drotar (1988), writing for paediatric psychologists, provides a useful summary of the findings of studies to date. He summarises some of the many factors significant in failure to thrive and points out important differences in aetiology and therefore treatment, depending on the time of onset of FTT. He goes on to summarise dimensions of assessment (such as developmental, family, feeding, parent–child interaction). He also proposes a two-tier treatment model consisting of 'core' treatment for all FTT children (paediatric care with periodic home visit follow-up) and specialised, more intensive services for some. Psychosocial treatment might be instigated, where each aspect of treatment could be varied in terms of the following: the main focus (e.g. child, parent); the target area for improvement (e.g. physical growth, cognitive development); the context (hospital, community); and the general goals (e.g. enhancement of child development, of parent–child relationship, improved family functioning). He usefully stresses the importance of interventions such as advocacy to help FTT families resolve crises concerning housing, money and food for those who are economically disadvantaged, hence paying attention to the potential significance of environmental factors in failure to thrive. Such a treatment model necessarily draws upon the expertise of a range of disciplines. It also attends to the fact that FTT children are not a homogeneous group; a variety of factors may contribute to any one child's FTT.

Frank and Zeisel's (1988) extensive review of the FTT literature summarises treatments as having two potential dimensions: a nutritional dimension (with the aim of promoting compensatory 'catch-up' growth) and a psychosocial dimension (focusing on the particular stressors faced by any one family). In order to encompass both dimensions, a multidisciplinary response would normally be required. This would ensure input from a range of professionals who, by virtue of their varied professional perspectives, are more likely to address the FTT from both the psychosocial and nutritional perspectives than any single profession.

More recent overviews include that by Hanks and Hobbs (1993), addressing paediatricians. They highlight the complex medical, social and psychological factors which contribute to a child failing to thrive and the necessity for a multidisciplinary perspective on assessment and treatment. They conclude that for assessment, food diaries and video recording of mealtimes should be used to enable professionals to tailor interventions to the needs of each family.

Hobbs *et al.* (1993) address failure to thrive in the context of child abuse and neglect. They stress that the thrust of any treatment programme must be to correct malnutrition, whilst also addressing parenting issues and generally providing support and care for parents to enable them to achieve this goal. This approach fits with Frank and Zeisel's (1988) two-dimensional model of a nutritional and a psychosocial dimension to treatment. Hobbs *et al.* recommend assessment of food intake as an initial stage of treatment, followed by dietary advice. Observation of feeding is also recommended, preferably with a video recording which can then be reviewed to identify micro and macro level issues and hence develop interventions. All this is in the context of multidisciplinary work.

Nutritional intervention

Addressing the nutritional aspect of FTT is not unproblematic. Successful intervention generally requires more than simply giving nutritional advice. Nearly a decade after Frank and Zeisel's work, Moores (1997) writes from the perspective of an experienced dietitian. She stresses the ways in which nutritional advice for FTT children needs to differ from that for children growing normally. It is often necessary to overcome the resistance of parents (and sometimes professionals) to introducing the level of fats and sugars

POINTS FOR INTERVENTION

These overviews of FTT research and practice indicate the following:

- Assessment and intervention must take account of the multifactorial aetiology of FTT.
- The nutritional and psychosocial dimensions must be addressed at assessment and intervention; because of this, a multidisciplinary perspective on assessment and intervention is extremely valuable.
- Interventions should be shaped to the needs of each child and their family, on the basis of assessment.

needed to achieve the required calorie intake. Moores also warns against the use of supplements as it medicalises the problem, addressing the nutritional but not the psychosocial aspects of FTT. Such an approach may then preclude a broader, psychosocial perspective being accepted by the family at a later stage.

Other practitioners contacted for this review spontaneously referred to the importance of increasing intake of FTT children with 'real' food, not supplements. However, one health visitor reported local GPs prescribing FTT children high calorie supplements and then sending the families away. This course of action might be attributed to a lack of FTT resources in the area, or simply to a GP taking a narrow nutritional perspective on failure to thrive.

Growth outcomes from FTT intervention studies

Moving from the overviews to studies of specific FTT interventions, several studies over the past decade have reported their outcomes in terms of improved growth of FTT children.

Growth outcomes from single intervention studies

McCann *et al.* (1994) describe the 'management' (i.e. treatment) provided in Oxford to the families of 26 children referred to paediatricians for FTT by their GPs. Parents and children were seen monthly for between 3 months and 2 years, depending on the severity of problems. All children put on weight, with their mean weight deficit for height significantly improved compared with referral measures. The particular focus of this study was the eating habits and attitudes to body shape of the mothers of these FTT children. Although they did not suffer from clinical eating disorders, the mothers scored significantly higher on the restraint subscale of an eating disorders examination. All received a combination of dietary, feeding and management advice regarding their children's feeding difficulties, in the setting of an outpatient clinic. Although membership of the team providing treatment is not specified, it appeared to extend beyond input from paediatricians. For example, the authors report that staff explored the parents' attitude to food and examined how parents' attitudes influenced management of their children's feeding difficulties, suggesting input from psychologists or social workers. Thus interventions addressed both nutritional and psychosocial aspects, and all children put on weight, achieving a mean centile of the 5th centile.

A multidisciplinary feeding disorders team in Clwyd, Wales, developed in response to difficulties in assessment and hence treatment of feeding problems, has reported on its outcomes (Powell and Reid, 1994). They present clinical findings from 20 FTT children who were referred to the team. Outcome was assessed by converting weight at referral and discharge to standardised scores; the results of paired tests were highly significant suggesting that their approach is successful. Treatment starts with a domiciliary visit by members of the team, for a psychosocial and behavioural assessment. Food diaries are kept by parents and permission is obtained to videotape a meal. Each child is then brought to outpatients for weighing and measuring. A feeding management programme is negotiated with the parents, with copies to the GP, health visitor, community paediatrician and any others involved in giving feeding advice. Workers maintain contact through home visits and by telephone; parents and children also attend a family support group where the parents work alongside staff on effective child management strategies.

More recently, Hampton (1996) has reported on the evaluation of the work of The Children's Society's Infant Support Project with children under 3 years referred for failure to thrive. Outcomes for 108 children referred to the Infant Support Project were evaluated. Hampton reports that 68 per cent of the children with whom they worked made at least satisfactory progress in terms of their growth. The multidisciplinary team comprises nursery nurses, health visitors and social workers, all employed by the voluntary organisation which operates the team. At referral children are given an FTT score depending on the number of FTT indicators (physical, psychological and social) evident at the time of referral. A single team member is then allocated as worker, and all work with the family is conducted in their own home. However, the allocated worker can consult with team colleagues in the course of the work. A number of assessment visits (including video recording of two meals) are undertaken, with a focus on forming a working alliance with parents. Parents also complete a food diary. A summary of findings at assessment is given to the parents and forms the basis of a working agreement. This includes suggestions for work on both nutritional and psychosocial factors. Work proceeds in the home, on the basis of planned ignoring and positive reinforcement of behaviour, and is evaluated at the end of the course of work and 6 months after work has finished.

Hobbs and Hanks (1996) report on the outcome of the first 18 months work undertaken by their team. Their analysis showed that of the 47 children who attended on more than one occasion, only eight children deteriorated in terms of weight. For the rest there was an overall improvement from a mean Z score of -2.17 to one of -1.87 (with a Z score of -2 roughly equivalent to the 3rd centile). Those who improved included the four infants in the group whose FTT was most severe. The team was set up to provide a multidisciplinary approach within the health service for the treatment and management of infants and children who fail to thrive. A video recording of a mealtime at home is made and the dietitian undertakes a home visit for a full feeding history. Families are then seen at the clinic; two professionals work directly with each family whilst the others observe (with the family's permission). Routine laboratory investigation is not undertaken on every child. The team uses behavioural interventions, provides advice and support around feeding and diet, and undertakes community-based multidisciplinary work. When devising treatment, they emphasise the importance of psychological issues, especially the child–parent relationship.

Health visitor led intervention

Important work has been undertaken by the Parkin Project in the Newcastle area by Wright and her colleagues (Wright *et al.*, 1998b). They have conducted a randomised controlled trial to evaluate the effectiveness of community-based, health visitor led intervention for FTT children under 2. When last weighed for follow-up a year or more after intervention, 76 per cent of the intervention group had recovered from their FTT compared to only 55 per cent of the control group. Intervention group children were also reported to have better appetites than children in the control group. This project uses health visitors as the key workers, conducting home-based standardised assessments which include the child's medical and dietary history and then, with a paediatric dietitian, providing specialist advice on diet. For those children who do not recover, the health visitors join team meetings with a research paediatrician, liaison health visitor and dietitian to discuss future management. For the purposes of the randomised controlled trial, the health visitors in the control practices received no additional training but continued routine weighing of children at baby clinics. Despite limitations such as low response at follow-up, the findings suggest that enhanced health visitor input (with training and support from a specialist FTT team) can be successful compared with conventional health visitor management.

Studies comparing growth outcomes of different interventions

The preceding discussion focused on reported outcomes of various single intervention strategies. However, some studies compare outcomes from various interventions.

Sturm and Drotar (1989) assessed the effectiveness of three types of intervention – family-centred, parent-centred and advocacy groups – in terms of improved growth; they have also reported on cognitive development (Drotar and Sturm, 1988; see p. 65 below). They report on weight outcomes at age 3 years following interventions with 59 children with early histories of FTT. The mean age at intake was just over 5 months (ranging from 1 to 9 months) and all had been hospitalised for FTT. Each of the three interventions addressed psychosocial issues, although each had a different focus. All the interventions were home based and time limited, with input extending no longer than 12 months. Alongside this input every child was also under hospital care, so one might assume nutritional aspects were being addressed here. Regardless of the type of intervention they received, the majority attained normal weight-for-height although nearly one third demonstrated at least mild wasting. Most improvement occurred between intervention and age 12 months; thereafter they maintained the improvement to the final follow-up at 36 months. It was found that shorter duration of FTT prior to diagnosis and greater initial rate of weight gain following hospitalisation predicted weight-for-height at age 36 months. This suggests that early psychosocial intervention is particularly important in re-establishing appropriate weight-for-height in young FTT children.

Sullivan (1991) compared two interventions used by paediatric nurses with FTT children, to evaluate their relative efficacy in terms of improved growth. One intervention was solely nutritional, with mothers receiving calorie management input. Others received 'socioemotional growth fostering interventions', which focused on healthy mother–child interaction

POINTS FOR INTERVENTION

These studies of FTT interventions indicate that, for improved growth, interventions should:

- Be based on a thorough assessment, which includes a full feeding history, completion of a food diary and preferably a video recording of a mealtime.
- Attend to psychosocial as well as nutritional factors. Simply focusing on the latter may exacerbate problems.
- Establish a working agreement with the parents; there is some evidence that success depends on having this. Having such an agreement potentially empowers carers, providing a means by which they can be given credit for any success.
- Be conducted (at least in part if not fully) in the child's home and include participation of the parents as part of the intervention.
- Make use of health visitors who may be particularly well placed to undertake FTT work (if provided with additional, appropriate FTT training and support).
- Be speedy, since there is some evidence that the sooner the FTT is identified the more likely it is that catch-up growth will take place.

behaviours. Sullivan reports that a focus on nutritional intake seemed to exacerbate current mother–child conflicts, whilst children whose mothers received socioemotional growth fostering interventions showed greater weight gain and their mothers showed more behaviour conducive to improving growth. This provides further support for a two-dimensional model of intervention and suggests that a purely nutritional focus may be detrimental to mother–child interactions.

Cognitive development outcomes from FTT intervention studies

It is known that FTT can result in impaired cognitive development, in addition to stunted growth. Therefore studies which compare various interventions in terms of improved cognitive functioning as well as growth are particularly important.

Drotar and Sturm (1988) assessed the effectiveness of family-centred, parent-centred and advocacy groups in terms of improved cognitive development (as well as growth, as reported by Sturm and Drotar (1989) and cited above). Each of the three interventions addressed psychosocial issues. Drotar and Sturm found cognitive development declined between 5 and 36 months despite the treatment and there were no differences between any of the treatment groups in terms of cognitive status or growth. However, they conclude that their interventions (all relatively short-term) may not have been sufficiently powerful to have an impact. In addition, their selection criteria may have resulted in their sample (aged 1–9 months at onset of FTT) including two distinct types of FTT children. As discussed in Chapters 2 and 3, it has been established that infants whose failure to thrive begins when they are under 6 months may be very different from those whose FTT starts when they are over 6 months in terms of causal factors and hence treatment or intervention requirements. They also drew on a very particular clinical group of children for their sample; that is, children who had been hospitalised for FTT. The major methodological problems with those studies which draw their FTT sample solely from children who have been hospitalised have been discussed earlier (Chapter 1, p. 15).

Casey *et al.* (1994) undertook a large study of preterm infants with low birth weights. The study was unusual in that it was a prospective, randomised clinical trial. Undertaken in the USA for 3 years, its objective was to determine whether multifaceted intervention decreased the incidence of FTT and improved the subjects' 3-year intelligence, growth, health and behaviour. It would appear that this was a multidisciplinary approach since the intervention group children received home visits, and attended a child development centre and their parents attended group meetings; there was also ongoing medical follow-up (comprising medical, developmental and family assessment). The development and identification of FTT did not differ between the intervention and follow-up groups. However, children with FTT in the intervention group with higher compliance did demonstrate higher IQ at 3 years than both the low-compliance FTT children and those with FTT in the follow-up group, suggesting that a high level of input was effective in reducing the cognitive impairment which can be a consequence of FTT.

Findings from these two studies are inconclusive regarding features of intervention studies important for enhancing cognitive development. However, Casey et al.'s findings suggest that more than minimal input or participation by parents is necessary to have a significant impact on IQ. One could hypothesise regarding the reasons for high or low compliance and whether these factors might have been successfully addressed via other interventions such as advocacy.

Feeding disorders studies

Feeding problems or failure to thrive?

As discussed in the preceding chapters, food refusal in young children inevitably blurs into the domain of failure to thrive. Not all children with feeding problems will fail to thrive; nor will all children who fail to thrive necessarily have feeding problems. However, for some children feeding difficulties and failure to thrive will go hand in hand. Where they do, tackling feeding difficulties is often a successful strategy since such problems are often amenable to change.

The terms 'feeding problem' and 'food refusal' are sometimes used as equivalents for the term 'failure to thrive'. Some services may actually be designed for FTT children but are presented as targeting feeding difficulties (which are common amongst young children). This may have some advantages. For one thing, referral for work on food refusal is likely to be experienced by families as less stigmatising than dealing with *failure* to thrive. In addition, labelling services as tackling feeding rather than FTT may not only be important for families but also for those professionals who potentially refer families. As was discussed in Chapter 3, some health and social care workers erroneously assume that FTT is always associated with abuse and neglect and so would be deterred from referring the vast majority of FTT families (whose children are not abused or neglected, but are loved and well-cared for) to an FTT service.

Treatment of feeding problems was an important issue for a range of professionals contacted by the author for the purposes of this review. The blurring of the terms 'failure to thrive' and 'feeding problems' was immediately apparent. One respondent expressed the view that the term 'failure to thrive' was too wide and hence the focus of their work was feeding rather than FTT. Others used the terms interchangeably or reported working with 'children with feeding problems or FTT'. The co-ordinator of a team working with under-11s in an inner city area reported that feeding problems were regularly cited by health visitors as a reason for referral of young children to the team. Several paediatricians reported plans to develop or extend feeding clinics, in response to increasing demand for treatment of FTT and feeding disorders.

Feeding disorders studies which address intervention strategies with young children and were published over the past decade range from single case examples to reviews. Some of the studies are simply of young children with feeding problems and food refusal, regardless of their growth status, whilst others use the term as a synonym for failure to thrive.

Studies of interventions for feeding problems

In looking at studies of interventions for feeding disorders, one can immediately see some parallels between the core components of successful strategies for these interventions and for failure to thrive. Studies focusing on feeding difficulties stress the relevance of a full psychosocial assessment to inform intervention. Since infants or young children with feeding difficulties are not necessarily also failing to thrive, such studies do not always attend to issues of nutrition and diet. However, since food refusal is sometimes related to specific tastes or textures, even studies which did not include FTT children may touch on the means to assess and adjust the nutritional level of meals.

Case studies are of limited value in terms of the extent to which the findings may be generalised. However, that by Archer and Szatmari (1990) of Hamilton, Ontario, provides a usefully detailed report of their work with the family of a 4-year-old boy with food aversion. The authors highlight the importance of full assessment, including a history of feeding, before devising appropriate interventions.

During interviews with both parents, the authors learned from his mother that the child had been a premature baby, kept in the nursery longer than usual because of inconsistent sucking. He spat out solids (at 3 months) but his mother persisted until he accepted them at 5 months. With each new food he screamed, vomited or choked. At 6 months bottle feeding ceased, solids increased as did the vomiting. He did not chew well and had a 'fear' of lumpy foods. The mother reported that feeding was a battle, although observation of mealtimes revealed (now) normal feeding behaviour. She also reported that she was sexually and physically abused as a child and punished if she did not want to eat.

Treatment was multifaceted, integrating systemic, psychodynamic and behavioural concepts. In this case the work did not involve individual treatment of the child. The mother was given reading material and she recorded her child's eating; in addition she was given supportive counselling, with her anxieties accepted and recognised. By 6 months post-assessment the child was feeding himself all the time. The careful assessment process had enabled the authors to devise an intervention strategy which successfully addressed the key factors in this child's FTT, meeting the mother's need for counselling and advice whilst also changing mother–child interactions at mealtimes by means of behavioural interventions.

Taking a broader perspective than the case study, Harris and Booth (1992) provide a useful overview of the nature and management of eating problems in preschool children. They acknowledge, as discussed above, that feeding difficulties and failure to thrive are not necessarily synonymous. They suggest that children with chronic food refusal 'typically give strong, clear signals of dislike and refusal', whereas infants with a typical pattern of failure to thrive are described as 'showing a lack of competence in communicating clearly and unambiguously their needs during mealtimes' (p. 62).

Harris and Booth go on to say that diagnosis and management of feeding problems (as with failure to thrive) are beyond the expertise of any single professional group. They propose treatment using behavioural intervention strategies, implemented by a multidisciplinary team. Their model is essentially psychosocial. Its three components are reducing parental anxiety, acceding control of feeding to the child and educating the parent in social reinforcement techniques that will enhance appetite. Harris and Johnson (1997) have since suggested that a vital component of assessment for intervention in feeding difficulties is a complete history of feeding; for example, to ascertain whether there was late introduction of solids (which might then lead to development of oral-motor dysfunction).

Wolke and Skuse (1992) also write on infant feeding problems, but this time explicitly approach it as an important dimension of much FTT. They describe the work of their multidisciplinary clinic team in the UK, detailing its approach to the diagnosis and management of feeding problems. Assessment focuses on the feeding problem, the factors which precipitated it and those which maintain it. A standard child paediatric and neurological assessment is undertaken, combined with a full medical and feeding history, and anthropometric and developmental assessments. They also routinely evaluate oral-motor functioning. Dietary histories are obtained for those infants who are failing to thrive. Mothers are interviewed regarding their perceptions of their child's behaviour; psychiatric screening is only undertaken if there is evidence that this is appropriate. Feeding at home is filmed and mother–child interactions during a structured play session are observed. Their treatment approach is then primarily behavioural but incorporates family therapy or psychodynamic strategies where appropriate. The initial aim is to establish organised, regular, predictable mealtimes. They recommend that treatment is undertaken in the home environment although they suggest that an outpatient approach can be a viable alternative.

Similarly Skuse (1993), from his overview of studies of feeding problems, recommends behavioural techniques and social reinforcement (including peer modelling), rewarding feeding behaviour and ignoring everything else. He suggests strategies such as time-limited mealtimes, with children offered small quantities of foods they are known to like.

A thorough analysis of the physiology of feeding and the impact a feeding disturbance may have on infant behaviour and mother–infant relationships is provided by Ramsay (1995). She describes the practice at her multidisciplinary Feeding Disorders Clinic in Quebec, outlining her approaches to assessment and treatment. The clinic conducts a multidisciplinary assessment which consists of a medical, feeding, and psychosocial history; a nutritional and developmental assessment; and observation of mealtimes. Ramsay outlines four broad approaches to assessment and treatment used within her clinic, making the point that these two processes largely operate in tandem and should be conducted in a supportive and non-judgmental manner. The approach (or elements of approaches) selected depends upon the level of severity of the feeding disturbance. In brief, Approach I (used with mild to moderate feeding disturbance) consists of affirming parents' suspicions, educating them regarding the physiology of feeding, nutritional management and specific feeding techniques, and home-based behavioural management. Approach II is home-based therapy plus telephone support, office-based behavioural therapy with both parents, therapeutic handling of emotional conflicts, supportive parental counselling and behavioural guidelines to manage other maladaptive behaviour. Approach III includes parent–infant therapy and couple therapy, used when interactional and interpersonal issues are extremely problematic and the feeding problems judged untreatable. Approach IV consists of multi-service involvement, which may be used in conjunction with elements of Approaches I to III. Ramsay presents a case history to illustrate the clinic's work, although no information on outcomes from its work is presented.

A study comparing feeding problem interventions

From the perspective of feeding problems, there has been some useful work comparing different interventions. Turner *et al.* (1994) undertook a controlled treatment outcome study to compare the effects of behavioural parent training and standard dietary education on the mealtime interaction, feeding behaviour, nutritional status and adjustment of children with feeding disorders. Twenty children aged 18 months to 5 years were randomly assigned to treatments, having initially been screened by means of a medical assessment, behavioural observation, mealtime interaction, nutritional intake analysis and self-report measures of parent and child adjustment. At follow-up just 3–4 months later, children in both treatment groups showed improvement on child behaviour measures at home and in mealtime observations in the clinic and showed an increase in the variety of foods sampled, suggesting little difference in terms of overall outcomes for the two interventions.

However, Turner *et al.* did find that mothers who received parent training showed more positive mother–child interactions during mealtimes than did those just receiving dietary education. This finding suggests that parent training could have the potential for positively affecting children's development, although the picture might have been clearer if follow-up had been conducted later than a few months after intervention.

POINTS FOR INTERVENTION

These studies of feeding problems suggest that successful interventions should be designed with the following factors in mind:

- The use of a multidisciplinary team may be most effective, as assessment and intervention are beyond the expertise of any single professional group.
- A full assessment process is necessary, including a detailed feeding history, observation of mealtime (including a video recording) and an evaluation of oral-motor functioning. This assessment should also attend to the factors which now keep the FTT going (not just those that initially precipitated it).
- Intervention should be designed to meet the needs of each child and their family; this might result in work only with carers and not with the child.
- There is some evidence that home-based work is most effective.
- Behavioural intervention strategies can be particularly useful, but usually alongside other interventions (from nutritional advice to family therapy).
- Nutritional or dietary education alone may be of limited effectiveness.

SUMMARY

In conclusion, this chapter has drawn together findings from four types of intervention studies – overviews of FTT research, growth intervention studies, cognitive development intervention studies and feeding disorders studies. The key implications for practice for each group of studies have been given in the Points for Intervention (pp. 60, 64 and 71), apart from the cognitive development studies where findings were inconclusive. The overall findings from these groups of studies can be briefly summarised as follows:

- Both assessment and intervention must take account of the multifactorial aetiology of FTT, addressing nutritional and psychosocial factors.

- A multidisciplinary team may be best placed to provide the breadth of response necessary.

- Intervention needs to be staged and flexible, depending on aetiology. Ideally, it should start with the broadest, least intrusive strategy, and then use a staged approach with increased input according to the needs of the child/family.

- Assessment should be part of the overall intervention process.

- Assessment should include an understanding of parents' beliefs about and attitudes to food in general and their child's FTT in particular. Their attempted solutions and views of causes of the FTT must be understood. Only then can nutritional advice (if appropriate) be framed in a way which is acceptable to the family. Assessment should also include family/parent resources (emotional and material).

5
MODELS OF INTERVENTION
WHERE, HOW AND BY WHOM?

The previous chapter looked in detail at what is currently known about effective FTT and feeding disorders assessment and intervention. However, the content of an intervention – its steps or stages – is only part of the picture. What do we know about the most effective way of using these interventions? Does it matter where the intervention takes place? What about the manner in which the work is conducted? Does it matter who works with the family? This chapter examines these questions and then presents a model for assessment and intervention.

Where to treat: Home, clinic or hospital?

To date, FTT children and their families have been treated at home, in primary health and social care settings (such as a baby clinic or family centre), in hospital outpatient clinics and as inpatients. Since some of these resources are much more costly than others, what evidence is there regarding their relative effectiveness?

Hospital

There is evidence that hospitalisation alone provides a narrow response to FTT. Fryer (1988), in his meta-analysis of studies of hospitalisation, concludes that hospital may address the nutritional dimension of treatment since it influences physical growth of FTT children (approximately doubling their probability of catch-up growth). However, psychosocial development (which according to Frank and Zeisel's (1988) model should be the focus of the second dimension of treatment) is 'only modestly hastened' by hospitalisation. Fryer concludes by suggesting that it should not be the preferred treatment method, except when weight is at a dangerously low level.

Hobbs *et al.* (1993) have summarised the pros and cons of hospitalisation: they conclude that the majority of children can be adequately treated as outpatients. More recently, Wright *et al.* (1998b) found that a substantial number of children in their study of FTT were seen at hospital despite low levels of organic disease. They conclude that the savings from diverting such referrals could justify limited additional input for effective community-based management.

Clinic *vs* home

The relative efficacy of clinic-based compared to home-based work is an important issue. Whilst some of the studies in the preceding chapter were clinic based, many were home based fully or in part. Those providing home-based services often refer to the necessity of working in the home environment to be successful. However, this can be a relatively expensive option for the service providers (in terms of staff time and travel costs) compared to having the family attend a clinic. What evidence is there that home-based work is necessary for effective intervention, in terms of good growth and improved cognitive development?

Black *et al.* (1995) set out specifically to evaluate clinic plus home intervention compared to clinic intervention only for children under 2 years with FTT. All received services in a multidisciplinary growth and nutrition clinic; half also received home intervention from a community-based agency. This comprised weekly home visits for a year by lay visitors supported by a community health nurse. The work focused on giving support, promoting parenting, advising on child development, accessing resources and advocacy. The authors found that the children's weight improved regardless of intervention status. However, home intervention children had better receptive language and more child-oriented home environments over time. The youngest in this intervention group (aged under 1 year at recruitment to the study) also showed beneficial effects in terms of improved cognitive development. This led the authors to conclude that this model was effective with the youngest infants in the study, although the older children (that is, toddlers) may require an alternative model of home intervention.

The children from Black *et al.*'s study were then followed up when aged 4 years (Hutcheson *et al.*, 1997). On follow-up it was found that, more than one year after the home intervention finished, there were effects of the home intervention on motor development among all children. In addition, there were improvements in the cognitive development and behaviour during play of those children whose mothers reported low levels of negative affect towards their children. These findings indicate the importance of allowing for extended follow-up times to assess accurately the impact of such interventions. They also point to the value of home intervention in terms of enhanced cognitive ability.

The studies cited here provide limited evidence of the effectiveness of home-based as opposed to clinic-based work. Yet in the previous chapter several studies described using home-based work in preference (or in addition) to clinic-based interventions. Clearly, despite the lack of strong evidence to support claims for its effectiveness, many workers in the field of FTT believe home-based work to be crucial to successful FTT intervention.

Parents may be better able to carry through the changes required to get their child to consume more calories if they feel they have genuinely participated in the process of devising strategies for change. Many clinic-based interventions are, by definition, approaching FTT from a predominantly medical perspective – a perspective not renowned for its collaborative approach with parents, but tending towards a model of providing expert advice. Home-based interventions are often carried out by primary health or social care staff who may be more accustomed to working collaboratively with service users, engaging them in active partnership in negotiating working agreements.

It may not be home-based intervention *per se* that is crucial for enhanced growth and cognitive development. It may be that, by virtue of the work taking place in the home, certain aspects of assessment and intervention are necessarily better attended to than they might be in a clinic setting. Parents and children will be seen in their home environment, where workers are likely to build a much fuller understanding of the process of mealtimes than they would in a clinic setting. At home parents may feel less intimidated by the process than they might in a medical setting. They may be better able to express their concerns, to discuss their previously attempted solutions and to voice their views about suggested courses of action, including perhaps being better able to say 'no' to intervention strategies they feel unable to carry out. Such considerations take us on to an important but neglected area of research: that is, parents' views of FTT interventions.

How to treat: Parents' experiences of FTT interventions

Very little has been written about the experiences of parents whose children have been identified as failing to thrive and who have subsequently been part of a treatment or intervention programme. One exception is the paper by Miguel and Burton (1990) which relates the experiences of one family whose child was diagnosed as failing to thrive. For the time that this label was attached to their son's condition they felt that they were 'under the microscope' in terms of their parenting ability, which destroyed their sense of self-esteem.

Miguel and Burton conclude with the recommendation that a family systems model of evaluating any potentially FTT child and their family be used. Such a model moves beyond mother–infant interactions to look at wider family relationships in seeking to understand the processes by which an infant fails to thrive. They also recommend that the label 'failure to thrive' be eliminated because of the lay understanding that this implies failure, abuse or neglect by the parents. Finally, they highlight the need for information regarding the aetiology of FTT to be made more widely available to professionals and for networks of professionals in this field to be developed.

More recently, Neden (1996) has explored with a small group of mothers, some of whom had growth faltering children, their understanding of failure to thrive and views on what parents need from professionals to help them improve their child's growth. The group identified the need for better informed professionals offering better advice, support and non-stigmatising reassurance for parents. The mothers also highlighted a need for opportunities to discuss growth faltering with carers who have experienced similar problems, perhaps suggesting that group work with carers might be well received. Wright and Talbot (1996) make reference to group work with parents being provided by social workers linked to the Parkin Project in Newcastle (see also p. 63).

Some studies of intervention strategies have included an examination of parents' views but these are still few and far between. Exceptions are Hampton's (1996) report on a voluntary sector project working with FTT children and their families in their own homes. Project workers routinely ask parents to evaluate the service they have received at the end of work and 6 months later. Nearly 90 per cent of parents who completed anonymous evaluation questionnaires rated their contact with the project as good or excellent.

More commonly the literature refers to parents reporting being dismissed, fobbed off, given false reassurance, doubted or not being believed by professionals (e.g. Archer and Szatmari, 1990; Ramsay *et al.*, 1993; McCann *et al.*, 1994). Hobbs and Hanks (1996) have also made reference to carers feeling disempowered as they struggle with their FTT children. All these experiences are well illustrated in Case Study 5, describing the feelings and emotions of one set of parents as their daughter's FTT is investigated.

However, there appears to be a move towards working with parents, building them up so that the process of assessment and intervention is a positive rather than an undermining experience for them. As early as the 1980s, Hanks *et al.* (1988), in their small community-based intervention study, stressed the value of 'positive reframing' of the mother's and child's behaviour to reduce any sense of blame or guilt, and the importance of using interventions which allowed mothers to take credit for improvements. Likewise, Drotar (1988) stresses a partnership approach with parents, focusing on parental competence. Williams (1994) notes the importance of working with parents, and Powell and Reid (1994), in reporting on the work of their feeding clinic, highlight the need to establish from the parents' viewpoint what service characteristics are most important.

Bithoney *et al.* (1995), in a study looking at the relationship between parental stress, child psychosocial factors, anaemia, lead poisoning and growth deficiency in children, found that a strong sense of parental competence was associated with improved growth outcomes for children. Their findings confirm the importance of any intervention work in this field enhancing and not undermining parents' sense of their own competence. The work of Hampton (1996) and colleagues focuses closely on building positive working relationships with parents. As Hampton states:

> It is ... vitally important that they [the parents] are sufficiently empowered to take a real part in the process of negotiating the targets which make up the working agreement. (p. 266)

In summary, working in partnership with parents has become accepted practice in many areas of child health and social care in recent years, partly

Case study 5

Parents' experiences of FTT interventions

'She'll eat when she's hungry'; 'children don't starve themselves to death'; 'it's a phase – she'll grow out of it'; 'as long as she's drinking she'll be alright'. These were some of the clichés which Tom and Rebecca found particularly frustrating when they were used in relation to their young child's feeding difficulties.

Tom and Rebecca struggled for several months to convince health care professionals that their daughter Elaine was actually eating very little, and heard each of those phrases in that time. They were offered a range of advice by the different professionals they came into contact with – some of which was contradictory. The example which stuck in their minds was being told by their health visitor to offer Elaine a snack midway between her main meals, and then a doctor they saw a fortnight later for her immunisations told them not to give her anything between meals.

Tom and Rebecca described themselves as experiencing a rollercoaster of feelings and emotions: frustration and anger at their inability to adequately explain their concerns, increasing anxiety about Elaine – despite what they were being told, she was fading away before their eyes – and a growing sense that things were becoming out of control and so 'we must be doing something wrong'. The high points were associated with the good days when Elaine ate a little more, and the time when their new health visitor suggested that it might be a good idea for Elaine to be seen by a paediatrician.

Tom and Rebecca waited impatiently for the appointment with the paediatrician, hopeful that, at last, they would get some answers. They made several visits to the hospital, both for consultations and for Elaine to have a variety of tests. At what proved to be the last appointment, Tom and Rebecca were told that nothing had shown up in any of the tests, and that they should take Elaine home and 'feed her up'.

When describing this experience, Tom said that he felt they had been abandoned with nowhere else to turn for help and advice. Rebecca felt that her parenting abilities had been put under the spotlight and found wanting, and she reported a growing sense of despair.

as a result of the principles underpinning the Children Act 1989. The evidence suggests that building parental competence may be key to achieving the changes necessary to overcome a child's failure to thrive. It appears that work in the field of FTT intervention has begun to make some progress in terms of working collaboratively but still has a long way to go.

Who should treat: The case for multidisciplinary work

It is apparent from the discussion in Chapter 4 that many practitioners and researchers in the field of FTT and feeding disorders now recommend multidisciplinary work in both assessment and treatment. This recommendation is partly in response to the multifactorial aetiology of both conditions: they require the skills of a range of professionals.

Others who have very explicitly advocated a multidisciplinary approach include Benoit (1993), writing from the perspective of child and adolescent psychiatric services. She says that interventions may be infant-focused (such as behaviour therapy to resolve behavioural feeding disorders), mother-focused (primarily undertaken in clinical settings, in the form of individual psychotherapy), family-focused (particularly family therapy), or focused on the infant–mother relationship (aimed at improving the quality of caregiving). Benoit concludes that assessment and treatment are complex, and that they require a multidisciplinary team approach.

Similarly Marcovitch (1994) highlights the complexity of aetiology and suggests an attempt should be made at diagnosis of failure to thrive in physical, emotional, social and family terms. For those few children who have been both abused or neglected and suffer from FTT, they are also likely to be best treated by means of a multidisciplinary approach. Iwaniec (1996), writing primarily from the perspective of work with those FTT children who have been emotionally abused, acknowledges the need for a multidisciplinary response.

Hobbs and Hanks (1996), drawing from their clinical experience as part of a multidisciplinary team over the previous three years, identify two principles which guide their work: firstly, they consider that the management and treatment of FTT is rarely effective if dealt with by single professional input, and secondly, when the medical and psychological aspects of FTT are combined into a focus on feeding, then management and treatment become more effective.

One study has been conducted specifically to evaluate the effect of a multidisciplinary team approach (Bithoney *et al.*, 1991). The study, conducted in Boston, USA, compared growth outcomes for 53 FTT children referred to an outpatient multidisciplinary clinic with outcomes for 107 comparison subjects who attended a primary care clinic. The researchers concluded that multidisciplinary team treatment was more effective than treatment solely through a primary health care clinic, since at 6-month follow-up children treated by the team had a significantly higher growth quotient.

An additional strength of multidisciplinary teams identified in some of the literature is the mutual support provided within such a team setting. It is generally acknowledged that work with FTT children and their families is stressful not only for the parents but also for the professionals working with them. As Hobbs and Hanks (1996) concluded when writing about their multidisciplinary approach to FTT work:

> Such are the exhausting effects of supporting these needy and hungry children and their disempowered carers that it struck professionals with a long interest in this subject that to join forces might provide a way forward for an often intractable problem. (p. 284)

Structure and composition of multidisciplinary teams

The composition of those multidisciplinary FTT or feeding teams reported in the literature is varied, although there are some elements common to all. For example, Bithoney *et al.*'s (1989) team included paediatricians, nutritionists, a paediatric nurse, a child development specialist, a social worker and a psychiatrist or psychologist. Wolke and Skuse (1992) describe their team as comprising a child psychiatrist or paediatrician, a developmental or paediatric psychologist and a speech or dysphagia therapist. Their team can also draw upon a senior dietitian and a variety of other specialists (including social workers and a paediatric gastroenterologist). Ramsay (1995) suggested a multidimensional assessment by a multidisciplinary team comprising a nutritionist, occupational therapist, paediatrician, and psychiatrist or psychologist.

A number of teams specify the inclusion of health visitors. A specialist FTT team set up by a national children's voluntary organisation, The

Children's Society (Hampton, 1996), comprised nursery nurses, health visitors and social workers. Hobbs and Hanks' (1996) team comprised a health visitor, clinical psychologists, consultant community paediatrician, dietitian, community paediatrician and nursery nurse; they aim to be supportive to one another and to the parents with whom they work. Powell and Reid's (1994) multidisciplinary assessment and treatment team, which provides a service for preschool children with severe feeding problems, comprised a dietitian, paediatrician, play specialist, psychologist, health visitor, social worker and speech/language therapist. Wright *et al.* (1998b) report that their team comprises a liaison health visitor, research paediatrician and paediatric dietitian.

Contact with current FTT practitioners revealed many who worked in multidisciplinary teams, although their composition varied. These differences were partly reflected in team names; for example, 'Growth and Nutrition Clinic', 'Feeding Problems Team', 'Feeding Clinic', 'FTT Clinic'; 'Family Partnership Team'; 'Infant Support Project', 'Feeding Matters', and 'Growth Project'. The core membership of hospital-based or community health services teams was usually a paediatrician, specialist health visitor and dietitian. A number also had a psychologist as part of the team; some (especially those located within hospitals) also had input from a language and speech therapist. Teams established by or located within social services departments were more likely to include family workers as part of the team. One team (established to work with families of children under 11, only some of whom would have feeding problems) included an education welfare officer and school nurse; one of its joint funders was the education department. However, these contacts also revealed the extent to which team composition might change, either expanding as a result of increased demand or good evaluation work establishing their effectiveness, or contracting as a result of funding cuts and consequent loss of posts.

Contact with current practitioners working with FTT confirmed that a model of intervention which incorporates nutritional and psychosocial aspects is widely used (although rarely evaluated) by them. Even teams operating from a hospital base often manage to incorporate a psychosocial perspective by using input from psychologists and by including at least an element of home-based work (for example, by the psychologist making home visits or the family health visitor undertaking the work supervised by the specialist team).

Offering parents a choice of service also emerged as a theme from contact with practitioners. For example, a member of a multidisciplinary feeding clinic team located in a general hospital observed that some families and some professionals preferred their service, whilst others preferred to use the family centre service run by social services with a voluntary organisation. This links back with the discussion above of the relevance of consideration of parents' views of FTT interventions.

A model for effective FTT intervention

Failure to thrive potentially has long-term, negative effects which cannot be ignored, and therefore children who fail to thrive may be seen as falling within the broad definition of a child in need in the Children Act 1989 (Edwards *et al.*, 1994). Without the provision of services, a child who is failing to thrive is unlikely to 'achieve or maintain a reasonable standard of mental or physical health or of physical, intellectual, emotional, social or behavioural development' and 'their health or development is likely to be significantly or further impaired' (Section 17(10), Children Act 1989).

Since the Children Act 1989, there have been moves in the field of child health and social care towards more preventative work with families. This shift in focus, with its emphasis on parental support, may result in better and speedier responses to the needs of FTT children and their families. Certainly, with prompt and appropriate intervention, failure to thrive is often open to resolution.

Drawing on the evidence from research studies and the themes identified from discussions with current practitioners in the field of failure to thrive, a model for effective work with FTT children and their families is proposed below. However, such a model needs firstly to be developed within the context of a sound strategy for identification of young children whose growth is faltering.

Strategy for identifying children with poor growth

A major methodological problem with much FTT research is the lack of consistency regarding definitions of FTT (see Chapter 1). Use of clear, agreed definitions is equally important when developing protocols for FTT interventions. It is important that all workers involved in weighing and monitoring children use up-to-date charts, with careful attention being paid to charting preterm infants. With moves to parent-held records for young children, there are implications for systematic record-keeping in child health clinics to ensure that children's progress is noted and acted upon.

It is important that all professionals in health and social care work to the same charts and use the same definition in terms of thresholds for action. Such thresholds should not be tied to absolute centile position (e.g. below the 3rd centile) but rather to current growth rates relative to earlier growth, allowing for regression to the mean.

It should also be remembered that charts based on growth patterns of white Western children may be inappropriate for children of other ethnic groups, some of whom have different growth norms. All staff also need to be sensitive to different cultural practices in terms of infant feeding; these differences may relate to class, ethnicity or religion. In areas where there are high proportions of families for whom English is not their first language, it is important that either workers reflect the composition of the area (in terms of languages spoken) or bilingual workers be recruited to work with families.

Even with clear protocols and accurate charting, identification of FTT children may fall short if left to the discretion of health or social care professionals. It is known that, even when children's weights are known to health visitors, FTT children can pass unrecognised as such (Batchelor and Kerslake, 1990), although rates of identification have improved in recent years suggesting there is greater awareness amongst health professionals (Batchelor, 1996).

As discussed earlier, professional beliefs about FTT often link it with abuse or neglect, despite the fact that the two conditions rarely occur together. Such beliefs can deter professionals from identifying all FTT children, thus denying many children the opportunity to receive effective intervention and thereby re-establish growth and cognitive development. For this reason, using systems such as identifying children by means of a child health computer (Wright and Talbot, 1996) is advisable. However, such a system is not necessarily fail-safe: Wright et al. (1998b) report that compliance with their screening programme by health visitors was not universal. This perhaps points to the need for improved education and training of health and social care professionals about FTT, its aetiology (including the

POINTS FOR INTERVENTION

Drawing together the findings discussed in this section, important first steps which should ideally precede development of FTT interventions are:

- The development and adoption of protocols regarding the definition of FTT and of screening thresholds for poor growth in young children.
- The use of up-to-date, appropriate charts by all professionals.
- Provision of training in nutritional and psychosocial aspects of FTT to relevant health and social care staff, to enhance their skills in identification and assessment of FTT.

fact that the majority of FTT children are loved and well-cared for, not abused or neglected) and potential intervention strategies, particularly those addressing feeding problems.

Initial assessment and early intervention

Prompt assessment of and intervention for FTT is essential if the potential long-term effects of impaired growth and cognitive development are to be ameliorated. Primary health and social care staff are perfectly placed to identify FTT children, and ideally these staff should have training in both the nutritional and the psychosocial aspects of FTT. Studies such as that by Wright *et al.* (1998b) also point to the importance of such workers being supported by specialist FTT resources, such as a dedicated multidisciplinary FTT team.

With the move to parent-held child health records, it may be parents rather than health professionals who first identify that a child's growth is faltering. If this is the case, it is vital that professionals respond to these concerns; research cited earlier indicates that parents of FTT children have often experienced being 'fobbed off' or disbelieved (p. 77). For effective assessment and the planning of appropriate intervention strategies, careful attention needs to be paid to the parents' worries, their beliefs as to why the child is not growing and what they and others have already tried in order to overcome the problem. There is some evidence that this work is best conducted in the child's home and, at the very least, a mealtime at home should be observed (and recorded on video) as part of the assessment.

In many cases, it may be appropriate and possible to start with an educational approach by providing advice, if it is evident that parents are simply unaware of some aspects of their child's needs (for example, dietary advice to use full cream rather than skimmed milk). Such a model of intervention fits with the 'hierarchical' approach described by Wright and Talbot (1996). This model assumes that it is most appropriate to offer the least specialist (and least stigmatising) service first, unless the initial assessment clearly indicates otherwise. As noted in Chapter 4, even nutritional advice such as this needs to be given with care, with a full understanding of the parents' views about food. The need for sensitivity to parents' views was evident in Case Study 4, pp. 41-2. It may be necessary to counter current adult health messages about reducing levels of fat consumption, advertising campaigns such as that for cream cakes which describes them as 'naughty but nice', and commercial slimming regimes which label some types of foods as 'sins'.

To achieve the required change, it is vital that any advice given is provided in a manner which is experienced by the parents as supportive and which fits with their understanding of the problem. For example, if parents believe their child has a medical problem, advice about changes in feeding practices might only be 'heard' when delivered by a doctor. The same advice from a health visitor or family worker may never achieve the desired change.

POINTS FOR INTERVENTION

With sound strategies for training of staff and for identification of FTT children in place, a staged model of assessment and intervention can be developed:

- First stage by primary health and social care staff, undertaking an initial assessment and (in appropriate cases) providing nutritional advice.
- Second stage assessment and intervention in consultation with specialist FTT services (perhaps in the form of a multidisciplinary team).

Second stage assessment and intervention strategies

It may be that a child's growth does not improve with nutritional advice or primary care staff may have concerns that the FTT intervention required is beyond their immediate resources. If this is the case, then it is important that those staff have access to specialist FTT resources, preferably in the form of a multidisciplinary team to which they can refer. From the research and clinical literature it is clear that such a team should comprise members who share a perspective on FTT in terms of its nutritional and psychosocial aspects, perhaps achieved by interdisciplinary training.

This second stage of work (both assessment and intervention) should, in view of research findings and clinical practice recommendations, be at least partly home based. This might be achieved by one or more team member working with the family in their home. Alternatively a primary care worker, such as the family's health visitor who will have ongoing contact with and knowledge of home circumstances, may undertake work with the family under the direction of the team.

Second stage assessment of the child and family should then be undertaken. Assessment is not a one-off event but a process: if interventions provided at the first stage have proved unsuccessful this will inform the assessment of the aetiology of the FTT, not only in terms of what factors led to the initial problems but – more importantly – what factors or processes now keep it going. This assessment can then be used to inform which specialist FTT resources might be needed. It is important that such an assessment builds on the knowledge of the primary health care worker and referrer, and again incorporates the beliefs and views of parents on the causes of the FTT and their attempts to date to overcome it. The assessment should address the nutritional and psychosocial aspects of FTT and look at child, carer, social and environmental factors whilst maintaining an interactional perspective.

Dietary assessment

If not already conducted at the initial stage of work, then a dietary assessment might be undertaken. This could usefully include a food diary, although the potential inadequacies and inaccuracies of such diaries need to be recognised when calculating nutritional content. From the research evidence, it is clear that there is no case for invasive laboratory tests automatically being undertaken with FTT children. However, a detailed feeding history is essential and should be taken in relation to every FTT child.

Feeding skills assessment

Current feeding skills should also be assessed. Research evidence points to the importance of paying particular attention to the potential for feeding skills disorders (Ramsay *et al.*, 1993), as discussed in Chapter 3, pp. 43–6. Difficulties might be related to low level oral sensori-motor impairment, in which case the Schedule for Oral Motor Assessment (Reilly *et al.*, 1995) might be used. This schedule records oral-motor skills over a 20-minute observation of the infant being presented with a range of foodstuffs of varying textures. Further observation of mealtimes may be helpful to assess any feeding skills disorders and to build a fuller picture of parent–child interaction; video recording can again be of value. However, in assessing for such disorders, workers also need to be sensitive to the risks of medicalising problems by going down this route.

Assessment of family and social factors

Home observations can also form the starting point for an assessment of family dynamics and levels of social support, both of which may be significant in devising intervention strategies. Tools such as the HOME inventory (Caldwell and Bradley, 1984, cited in Skuse *et al.*, 1992) might be used to assess the quality of stimulation and support available to a child in the home environment. The Nursing Child Assessment Feeding and Teaching Scales (Lobo *et al.*, 1992; Barnard, 1978, cited in Skuse *et al.*, 1992) may be of value in rating caregiver–child interaction. Each scale contains six subscales measuring both parent and child behaviour during a defined situation such as feeding. The subscales measure behaviours such as a parent's response to their infant's distress and the infant's clarity of cues and responsiveness to parents.

Sensitive enquiry about the primary caregiver's eating habits, attitudes to food, personal experiences of abuse or levels of depression may be appropriate at this or subsequent stages of the work (McCann *et al.*, 1994; Stein *et al.*, 1995; Weston and Colloton, 1993).

Intervention strategies

Interventions may focus on the child, the carers, carer–child interactions, social or environmental factors, and any combination of these. At the broadest level, factors such as household income and adequacy of housing should not be ignored: successful resolution of a child's FTT may depend on recognising and addressing inadequacies of resources at this level. Interventions which pay scant attention to parental and family beliefs about a child's poor growth risk being unproductive if change in their interactions with their child (e.g. at mealtimes) is an element of the strategy. Work is likely to include sessions with parents and their child in the context of mealtimes, when modelling and behavioural techniques might be used. If assessment has identified personal issues for the parents then intervention may include work on an individual level, through one-to-one counselling, or work with the couple on their relationship. All this work may also be usefully supplemented with information about the nutritional and dietary needs of children. Finally, an underused intervention strategy is group work with parents of FTT children. It may have the potential to be effective but evidence is currently very limited and inconclusive; evaluation studies of such work are needed.

POINTS FOR INTERVENTION

To maximise the chances of success, assessment and intervention strategies should incorporate the following:

- At least some of the work with families being undertaken in their own homes.
- Close attention being paid to parents' views and beliefs regarding their child's FTT, to their attempted solutions and to what now keeps the FTT going (rather than what got it started).
- A model of assessment and intervention which encompasses nutritional and psychosocial aspects of FTT and which maintains an interactional focus, assessing the child, the carer and environmental factors singly and together.
- Creation of a multidisciplinary FTT team whose members have undertaken joint training in FTT causes, effects and interventions.

There is a need to provide a range of services which can then be packaged into an intervention strategy tailored to meet the needs of any particular child and their family. The package provided should, within resource limits, depend on salient current factors in that particular child's continuing FTT and allow for some degree of user choice. Attention should be paid not only to the content of the intervention strategy but also the manner in which it is applied. For example, are caregivers encouraged to participate, given credit for success, and generally likely to experience the interventions as supportive rather than undermining of their role? On the few occasions when it becomes evident that the FTT is occurring in an abusing or neglectful family environment, then workers need to be clear about procedures for referral to relevant child protection practitioners.

SUMMARY

- Hospitalisation of FTT infants should only occur when their weight is dangerously low.

- There is some evidence that home-based work can enhance children's motor and cognitive development. Many FTT workers advocate some home-based work, as the most appropriate setting for assessment of mealtimes and full understanding of parents' concerns and views on intervention strategies.

- Few studies have looked at parents' views on interventions with their FTT children. Recent studies, though, have emphasised the need to work with parents in a manner that creates a context for change: avoiding blame, acknowledging concerns, building on strengths and working in partnership.

- A multidisciplinary approach to assessment and treatment of FTT is the best means of ensuring that the nutritional and psychosocial dimensions are addressed.

- Effective FTT intervention depends, in the first instance, on sound strategies for identifying all children with poor growth. Ideally this would involve adopting protocols regarding the definition of FTT and of screening thresholds for poor growth, with appropriate use of up-to-date charts by all professionals.

■   Initial assessment and early intervention are best conducted by primary care workers, with support from FTT specialists. For some families, sound nutritional advice may be sufficient to achieve change.

■   If difficulties persist, a fuller assessment of diet, feeding skills, family and environmental factors may be necessary. Interventions should then be tailored to meet the needs of each child and their family.

6

CONCLUSIONS AND RECOMMENDATIONS

This review of current FTT research and practice has drawn on over a hundred publications, ranging from specific FTT intervention studies via general FTT and feeding disorders research on causes through to clinical writings addressed at FTT practitioners. This final chapter starts with some reflections on the key findings of the preceding chapters and moves on to discuss ways of developing best practice in the context of current provision. It concludes with recommendations that would ensure effective FTT services.

Key issues

Dialogue between researchers and practitioners

In recent years there have been several positive developments in FTT research and practice. Failure to thrive has had a higher profile amongst health and social care professionals, leading to improvements in identification of FTT children. Improved charts have also been developed, based on up-to-date standards. In addition, epidemiological studies such as those by Skuse and colleagues have been undertaken to accurately identify rates of FTT in the population. The rates revealed in these studies point to a clear overrepresentation of disadvantaged and abused or neglected children in clinical samples of FTT children. Despite this work, it is evident that many clinical practitioners continue to assume that FTT is always the result of abuse or neglect. This indicates the need for improved dialogue between researchers and practitioners, particularly with regard to dissemination of research findings.

An improved dialogue might also result in a better understanding of all aspects of FTT, including changes in definition and new thinking about causality. The gradual shift from simplistic definitions of FTT based on a child's absolute position on a weight centile chart (namely, below the 3rd centile) to definitions based on growth over time is filtering through to practitioners. However, the view that non-organic FTT is caused by maternal deprivation, now largely abandoned by researchers, still persists in some settings. This may account for some parents of FTT children experiencing the process of assessment and treatment as undermining and blaming of their parenting.

Practitioners' definitions of FTT have also had a profound effect on research. As shown in this review, the use of widely different definitions of FTT makes comparison of findings extremely difficult. Similarly, extensive use of clinical samples and inappropriate inclusion of preterm and small-for-dates infants in studies have limited the possibility of drawing any conclusions from this work.

There is a need for greater use of replication studies and cross-centre, population-based and theory-driven research in the field of psychological research into a range of paediatric conditions, including FTT (Drotar, 1994). The recent epidemiological studies by Skuse and his colleagues have made a valuable contribution to our understanding of FTT and have helped dispel some clinical misconceptions about prevalence and causality. These authors have also highlighted areas for future research, such as the need for studies that pay attention to the role of the FTT infant in the interactions between them and their carers (Boddy and Skuse, 1994). More recently, they identified the need for prospective studies to determine the causal nature of the association they found between infant development after growth faltering and mothers' problem-solving ability (Boddy, 1997).

Such work then needs to be supplemented by further studies on effectiveness of interventions. For example, the case has been made for home-based intervention (see Chapter 5), yet little is known about why location of intervention impacts on effectiveness. It may be that clinic-based intervention which pays very close attention to working collaboratively with parents could be as successful as (but less costly than) home-based work. More research is needed to answer such questions.

Here too there needs to be improved communication, not only between researchers, but also between researchers and practitioners. Ideally this would be a two-way communication, with exchange of ideas about past findings and future directions. Clinicians are perfectly placed to identify new research questions which may usefully be used by researchers who are in a position to design methodologically sound studies. Researchers have a responsibility to ensure that findings are then disseminated in a manner that makes them accessible to practitioners. Clinicians in their turn should ensure that their practice is in line with current research findings about causality and effective intervention.

Understanding of the importance of FTT

Research has now established that the effects of FTT include, in the short term, stress for caregivers and others trying to resolve a child's poor growth and any associated feeding difficulties. In the long term, effects include the possibility of serious adverse consequences for the child, such as stunted growth, impaired cognitive development, as well as disrupted family relationships.

There is now evidence that the timing and severity rather than the duration of a growth faltering episode is most important in terms of growth outcome, with infants whose FTT began when they were under 6 months of age at particular risk. Responses to FTT therefore need to be prompt, if intervention is to be made available to those children at greatest risk of poor outcome. Despite this knowledge, the experience of some parents of FTT children is that they are fobbed off or given false reassurances about their children's growth. At the opposite extreme, others immediately find themselves 'under the spotlight' in terms of their parenting, quickly caught up in a process which has been reported as disempowering and distressing.

An improved understanding amongst health and social care profes sionals, as well as parents, about the causes of FTT could go a long way towards improving the process of assessment and treatment or intervention. From studies of FTT it is apparent that failure to thrive is not generally part of the abuse/neglect spectrum, although some professionals still firmly place it there. Failure to thrive is due to inadequate nutrition, but many factors may contribute (individually or in combination) to a particular child failing to thrive. Predisposing child factors include being either a very sleepy child, undemanding of feeds, or a particularly restless child. The significance of feeding problems in FTT has been fully recognised over the last decade, and oral-motor skills deficits may play a part in feeding problems for some FTT children.

Development of better models of assessment and intervention

These findings highlight the importance of assessment of any child with poor growth including a thorough history of feeding and observation of current feeding practices. A sound assessment should also address the variety of factors that may limit a parent's capacity to provide the compensatory parenting needed to overcome a particular child's propensity to fail to thrive (such as a mother's own experience of an eating disorder). However, such an assessment requires time and sensitivity on the part of the health or social care professional, as well as an understanding of the multifactorial aetiology of FTT.

Sound skills in identification, assessment and treatment of FTT can only be developed through the provision of training in the nutritional and psychosocial aspects of FTT for relevant health and social care staff. Such training needs to operate in tandem with the development and adoption of protocols regarding the definition of FTT and of screening thresholds for poor growth in young children.

On the basis of research findings it is clear that work with FTT children should, in part at least, be undertaken in their own homes, with close attention being paid to parents' views on the causes and their attempted solutions. The model of assessment and intervention needs to encompass nutritional and psychosocial aspects of FTT and workers should maintain an interactional focus, assessing the child, the carer and environmental factors singly and together.

Developing best practice

Clearly measures of effectiveness and efficiency are important when developing intervention strategies for FTT children. As discussed in the preceding chapter, the different elements required to ensure that a service is effective in resolving FTT are gradually becoming clearer. In view of its multifactorial aetiology, it should come as no surprise that a multidisciplinary approach which focuses on an ecological or interactive model of FTT rather than a linear model of cause and effect is most effective. As Boddy and Skuse (1994) state:

If failure to thrive is to be considered as a syndrome, rather than a collection of symptoms, we must consider each aspect of its multi-dimensional aetiology in detail, while acknowledging that *no one factor in itself is causal.* (p. 403, author's italics)

Effective FTT services

Improving identification

For services to be effective, it is important that identification of FTT is wide ranging and then followed by thorough assessment of the aetiology of each child's FTT. Unless this happens there is a risk that professionals will only identify 'pockets' of FTT, and develop intervention strategies which might only be appropriate for that small part of the FTT spectrum which comes to their attention. This could deprive the majority of FTT children of the opportunity to re-establish an appropriate rate of growth.

From discussions with current practitioners, it is clear that there is scope for development of stronger links between those working with young children with poor growth and associated feeding problems and those working with children of all ages with learning difficulties or special needs such as cerebral palsy, many of whom have feeding problems. Such links could result in improved effectiveness of services as workers share and so develop their expertise in identification and assessment of feeding problems.

Multidisciplinary work

Multidisciplinary work has been identified as a potentially effective way of providing services for FTT children and their families. However, the meaning and interpretation of 'multidisciplinary work' can vary enormously. At best multidisciplinary teams work in a genuinely collaborative way, both between team members and with service users. It is salutary to note here that little can be said about parents' views on best practice in FTT assessment and intervention, since it appears from the literature that they are rarely asked. At worst multidisciplinary work can be an approach dominated by one profession (or one member of that profession) with a particular view on the most significant factor in FTT, to the exclusion of alternative perspectives.

It is perhaps inevitable that the focus of any team's work will be influenced by its composition, in terms of the professions represented, hierarchies within and between those professions and who 'owns' or controls the team. For example, the balance between the nutritional and psychosocial aspects of treatment may vary from team to team. Hospital-based teams headed by paediatricians may tend to give priority to the nutritional dimension, with a medical model of treatment. Some may include input on psychosocial perspectives by having a psychologist or family therapist as a team member or have access to such resources; others may pay scant attention to this dimension.

In contrast to this model, community-based teams, especially those which have (or had) a child protection focus or are funded by social services, are likely to pay close attention to psychosocial elements. They will probably work in partnership with parents, base much of their work in the home, and may well use group work as well as individual work. Such teams may then choose to draw on support from paediatricians, dietitians and speech therapists for a medical perspective to their work, so ensuring that the nutritional dimension of FTT is also addressed. Others may fail to assess and intervene on anything other than the psychosocial dimension.

A prerequisite for successful multidisciplinary work is a level of mutual respect and understanding across the professions sufficient for trust in each other's judgements. This is likely to be fostered by the experience of joint training, as evidenced in the child protection field where such a training model is common. However, being prepared to contribute to or undertake joint training requires a belief in its value. Professional rivalries, or a strongly held belief that you are right and therefore alternative perspectives are by definition wrong, could present major stumbling blocks to such developments. Each profession requires the humility to acknowledge that they may only have expertise in assessing and intervening in certain aspects of FTT and that they need other professions to ensure they provide a fully rounded assessment and intervention programme. A freedom from fears that other professions will, as a result, 'take over' another's role is also needed. These are significant factors at a time of budgetary constraint in the field of health and social care, when posts may be under threat if there are opportunities for the work to be moved to others.

Efficiency of services

Cost of using multidisciplinary teams

Turning now to efficiency, the issue of the cost of running any multi-disciplinary team is significant. There is anecdotal evidence from practitioners that some of the existing multidisciplinary FTT teams are shrinking; in particular loss of psychology input is reported. This is ironic in view of Boddy and Skuse's (1994) conclusion that methodological limitations to past FTT research have in part been exacerbated by the failure to attend to developments in mainstream psychology.

Bringing together a number of highly qualified professionals is an expensive task. Development of a model of staged interventions (such as that proposed in Chapters 4 and 5, and by Ramsay, 1995 and Wright and Talbot, 1996) is not only appropriate in view of FTT's multifactorial aetiology; it also makes sense in terms of only drawing on the most expensive resources in the most difficult situations. Developments in this direction might be fostered by means of interdisciplinary training so that each team member has sufficient grounding in both nutritional and psychosocial aspects of FTT to undertake initial assessment and early stages of intervention work. Appropriately trained and supported health visitors or family workers, for example, might carry out these initial tasks.

The context of FTT provision

Unfortunately there are factors which may be working against providing specific resources for children who are failing to thrive at present, including the funding of multidisciplinary teams. The creation of numerous small unitary authorities and health trusts in the 1990s has made setting up and funding services problematic. At times of budget cuts, local authority social services departments may resist identifying children who are failing to thrive as 'children in need' in the terms of the Children Act 1989, especially when it has been established that generally FTT is not part of the child abuse spectrum. However, recent moves to raise the profile of family support and preventative work, rather than focusing solely on child protection (Department of Health, 1995), may provide greater opportunities for social services departments to work in this field.

In addition, recently there have been important developments in health provision. There has been some amalgamation of trusts into larger units, and primary care groups have been created. These groups give general practitioners more influence over the development of community services. It remains to be seen whether this results in a raising of the profile of FTT identification and intervention.

Evaluation

With moves in the field of health and social care towards evidence-based practice, it is not only important that new services are developed in line with research evidence on effectiveness but also that steps are taken to evaluate all such services. Auditing of outcome should be standard practice. An essential element of such evaluation should be the views of users. As FTT services are primarily for infants and very young children, the views of parents and carers should routinely be sought. However, it should not be assumed that young children's views cannot be obtained. There have been important developments in recent years towards enabling children to participate in research: even quite young children may be enabled to express their views on the services they receive.

Funding can jeopardise the future of specialist services such as those for FTT children. Such difficulties may be compounded when practitioners are not evaluating their work in the field of FTT; if they cannot show evidence of effectiveness of working practices in terms of outcomes achieved they may not be well placed to argue for increases in (or even maintenance of) resource levels.

Examples of good practice

Despite the difficulties described above of developing sound FTT interventions, it is clear that innovative, research-based, effective and efficient services for FTT children are being run in the UK.

Good examples of FTT services include the Community Growth and Nutrition Service in Newcastle and The Children's Society's national 'Feeding Matters' programme, to name just two. Although they use very different models of delivery and only assess effectiveness of intervention in terms of improved growth and not cognitive development, each incorporates several of the key elements established in this review as necessary for effective work. They both use a multidisciplinary approach which includes a thorough assessment of nutritional and psychosocial factors, and provide (or train in) a range of interventions including behavioural approaches to feeding problems. Their approach is based on working at least in part in the child's home and always in collaboration with parents. Each has been developed on the basis of evidence-based research and workers are committed to evaluation of the services they provide, so they are well placed to develop, improve and, if necessary, justify their working practices. It is to be hoped that, on the basis of evidence presented in this review, more developments such as these will take place.

Future developments

There have been recent moves to bring together the range of disciplines working with or having responsibility for children (Audit Commission, 1994) which could bode well for future FTT work. The Audit Commission recommended, as a means of improving surveillance of children's sight and hearing, that coordinators be appointed. In view of the conclusions drawn from this review of FTT research and practice, there is a strong case to be made for the appointment of infant growth coordinators (Batchelor, 1996). They could be responsible for a programme of surveillance of the growth of young children, with automatic and speedy follow-up of those who fall below agreed screening thresholds. Such a move could go a long way towards ensuring that poorly growing children are identified more accurately and swiftly than at present.

There is now a requirement under the Children Act 1989 that children's services plans are jointly drawn up by health, social services and education departments, in consultation with voluntary sector service providers. These service plans should, in time, result in better coordinated provision for young children, including those who are failing to thrive. If these FTT services are developed along the lines suggested by current research studies then the likelihood that all FTT children and their families will receive appropriate and effective interventions will be greatly enhanced.

Recommendations

In conclusion, for good practice in FTT identification and intervention to be established, the following points need to be addressed:

- Failure to thrive needs to be on the agenda of child care and child health professionals. Raising the profile of child growth as a public health issue may best be achieved by appointment of infant growth coordinators at district or regional level.

- Common criteria for FTT need to be adopted, alongside development of protocols for FTT interventions based on best practice.

- Timing of developmental checks needs to be standardised (and perhaps their frequency increased) to allow for early identification of FTT, combined with routine assessment of the feeding skills and difficulties of slow growing infants (preferably by means of observation of a feed/mealtime).

- Health and social care staff working with young children with FTT require training in its causes and in effective models of intervention.

- Ideally, multidisciplinary FTT teams should be established to support primary health and social care workers and to undertake the more specialised pieces of FTT work.

- Improvements in the dialogue between researchers and practitioners are necessary, to ensure that practitioners are kept abreast of current developments in good practice and that researchers address questions that are of relevance to FTT practitioners.

- All FTT intervention work should include an evaluation of outcomes, so that questions of effectiveness and efficiency can be addressed.

With such steps in place, all FTT children could be provided with the opportunity to achieve the changes necessary to re-establish weight gain and so minimise the long-term effects of poor growth in early childhood.

Appendix

RESEARCH STUDIES OF INTERVENTION PROGRAMMES

Archer, L. and Szatmari, P. (1990) 'Assessment and treatment of food aversion in a four year old boy: a multi-dimensional approach.' *Canadian Journal of Psychiatry*, **35** (August), pp. 501–5.

TYPE OF STUDY   Single case study.

DEFINITION OF FTT   'Food aversion'; age 3.7 years at referral (though assessed by nutritionist as 'growing appropriately').

SAMPLING FRAME/SIZE/DRAWBACKS   Single case study.

CONTROL/COMPARISON GROUP   None.

TYPE OF TREATMENT/THEORETICAL RATIONALE/WHO PROVIDES   'Multi-faceted': parental education (reading material); child self-feeding; anxiety-management with mother; cognitive restructuring with mother re anxieties. Used 'supportive counselling approach'. Approach used 'psychodynamic, systemic and behavioural concepts'.

FOCUS OF TREATMENT (CHILD? CARER?)   Child; mother; couple (limited).

LOCATION OF TREATMENT   Clinic; Ontario, Canada.

FOLLOW-UP PERIOD   Six months post-assessment.

OUTCOMES/EVALUATION (WHAT DEFINITION?)   Feeding himself; Children's Eating Behavior Inventory scores dropped; no change on Achenbach Child Behaviour Checklist or on Parenting Stress Index.

Bithoney, W. G., McJunkin, J., Michalek, J., Egan, H., Snyder, J. and Munier, A. (1989) 'Prospective evaluation of weight gain in both non-organic and organic failure to thrive children: an outpatient trial of a multi-disciplinary team intervention strategy.' *Journal of Developmental and Behavioral Pediatrics*, **10** (1), pp. 27–31.

TYPE OF STUDY   Prospective evaluation.

DEFINITION OF FTT   Either length and weight below 5th centile *or* fallen across two standard deviations of growth chart (although not below 5th centile), corrected for genetic endowment.

SAMPLING FRAME/SIZE/DRAWBACKS   First 68 children with non-organic failure to thrive (NOFTT) referred to clinic over 15-month period minus four children without 6-month follow-up; all 22 organic failure to thrive (OFTT) children referred (over longer time period). Aged 3–72 months (mean 25 months; 70% <2 years).

CONTROL/COMPARISON GROUP   Comparisons made between outcomes for organic and non-organic FTT children, all of whom received same treatment.

TYPE OF TREATMENT/THEORETICAL RATIONALE/WHO PROVIDES   Multidisciplinary: paediatricians, nutritionists, paediatric nurse, child development specialist, social worker, psychiatrist/psychologist. Children given high calorie diet tailored to catch-up growth needs and food preferences, plus early intervention programme for developmental delay; behavioural therapies prescribed for feeding problems; social worker tackled social problems.

FOCUS OF TREATMENT (CHILD? CARER?)   Child; carer; dyad.

LOCATION OF TREATMENT   Growth and Nutrition Clinic in children's hospital; Boston, USA.

FOLLOW-UP PERIOD   Six months after initial clinic visit.

OUTCOMES/EVALUATION (WHAT DEFINITION?)   All showed catch-up growth on growth quotient. Authors conclude weight gain on therapeutic intervention was no way to diagnose NOFTT, and there was value in giving *all* the children high calorie diet plus work on psychosocial interactive problems.

Bithoney, W. G., McJunkin, J., Michalek, J., Snyder, J., Egan, H. and Epstein, D. (1991) 'The effects of a multidisciplinary team approach on weight gain in nonorganic failure-to-thrive children.' *Journal of Developmental and Behavioral Pediatrics,* **12** (4), pp. 254–8.

TYPE OF STUDY   Comparison of outcomes for children referred to a multidisciplinary, consultative outpatients' clinic and those treated in a primary care clinic.

DEFINITION OF FTT   Either length and weight below 5th centile *or* fallen across two standard deviations of growth chart (although not below 5th centile), corrected for genetic endowment.

SAMPLING FRAME/SIZE/DRAWBACKS   53 NOFTT children referred to outpatients and comparison group of 107 NOFTT children attending a primary care clinic.

CONTROL/COMPARISON GROUP   Comparison group.

TYPE OF TREATMENT/THEORETICAL RATIONALE/WHO PROVIDES Multidisciplinary outpatient FTT consultative clinic.

FOCUS OF TREATMENT (CHILD? CARER?) Children and carers.

LOCATION OF TREATMENT Clinic-based team work; Boston, USA.

FOLLOW-UP PERIOD Six months after treatment.

OUTCOMES/EVALUATION (WHAT DEFINITION?) Growth quotient for sample was 1.75 ± 0.39 SD; for comparison group was 1.18 ± 0.42 SD, $p < 0.001$, leading authors to conclude that the use of a multidisciplinary team offers special advantages in the rapid correction of undernutrition in children with NOFTT.

Black, M.M., Dubowitz, H., Hutcheson, J., Berenson-Howard, J. and Starr, R.H. (1995) 'A randomized clinical trial of home intervention for children with failure to thrive.' *Pediatrics*, **95** (6), pp. 807–14. ⠆

TYPE OF STUDY/LOCATION Evaluation of home-based intervention; randomised clinical trial.

DEFINITION OF FTT Weight for age below 5th percentile at 2 years or younger, having had birth weight appropriate for gestational age (minimum 36 weeks gestation).

SAMPLING FRAME/SIZE/DRAWBACKS Children recruited from an urban paediatric primary care clinic; most being raised by single African-American mothers on public assistance. 130 children fitted criteria and were randomly allocated to clinic plus home intervention (64) or clinic only.

CONTROL/COMPARISON GROUP 66 children received clinic-only intervention.

TYPE OF TREATMENT/THEORETICAL RATIONALE/WHO PROVIDES All children received services in a multidisciplinary growth and nutrition clinic. A community-based agency provided weekly home visits for a year by a lay visitor supervised by a community health nurse. Visits focused on giving support, promoting parenting, child development, accessing resources and advocacy.

FOCUS OF TREATMENT (CHILD? CARER?) Child and carer.

LOCATION OF TREATMENT Clinic/home in vicinity of Baltimore, USA.

FOLLOW-UP PERIOD 89% of families (116 of 130) completed one year evaluation.

OUTCOMES/EVALUATION (WHAT DEFINITION?) Children's weight for age, weight for height and height for age improved significantly during the 12-month study period, regardless of intervention status. The home intervention group children had better receptive language over time and a more child-orientated home environment. Younger children (under 1 year) receiving home intervention showed enhanced cognitive development. The authors conclude that their findings support cautious optimism regarding home intervention (provided by lay visitors) during the first year of children's life.

Casey, P. H., Kelleher, K. J., Bradley, R. H., Kellogg, K. W., Kirby, R. S. and Whiteside, L. (1994) 'A multifaceted intervention for infants with failure to thrive: a prospective study.' *Archives of Pediatric and Adolescent Medicine*, **148** (10), pp. 1071–7.

TYPE OF STUDY   Three-year, prospective study, randomised, clinical trial to determine whether a multifaceted intervention decreased the incidence of FTT in a group of preterm infants with low birth weights and improved the 3-year intelligence, health, growth and behaviour status of the children with FTT.

DEFINITION OF FTT   Postnatal growth deficiency measured by poor weight gain; weight less than 5th percentile for gestation-corrected age at two or more points in time; and rate of weight gain during preceding months less than average for gender and gestation-corrected age.

SAMPLING FRAME/SIZE/DRAWBACKS   914 preterm infants with low birth weight, fitting study criteria and born at one of eight university hospital sites.

CONTROL/COMPARISON GROUP   Infants randomly allocated to two levels of intervention.

TYPE OF TREATMENT/THEORETICAL RATIONALE/WHO PROVIDES   Intervention group children received home visits (weekly for the first year, then fortnightly), attended a child development centre up to 5 days a week from the age of 12 months and their parents attended group meetings every other month. All children (intervention and follow-up groups) received medical follow-up.

FOCUS OF TREATMENT   Child; carer.

LOCATION OF TREATMENT   Arkansas, USA.

FOLLOW-UP PERIOD   Three years.

OUTCOMES/EVALUATION (WHAT DEFINITION?)   At age 3 all children were assessed by raters blind to their FTT status, using instruments such as the Stanford-Binet Intelligence Scale and the Child Behaviour Checklist. Children with FTT in the intervention group with higher compliance demonstrated higher 3-year IQ and better behaviour scores than children with FTT in the low-compliance group. The development and identification of FTT did not differ between the intervention and follow-up groups, with 20–22% of children in each group developing FTT.

Drotar, D. and Sturm, L. (1988) 'Prediction of intellectual development in young children with early histories of non-organic failure to thrive.' *Journal of Pediatric Psychology*, **13** (2), pp. 281–96.

TYPE OF STUDY/LOCATION   Controlled study of efficacy of early intervention on the intellectual development of NOFTT children; children randomly assigned to one of three interventions. Also assessment of efficacy of multivariate predictive model of cognitive development including four domains (biological factors; characteristics of NOFTT; intellectual competence; environmental factors).

DEFINITION OF FTT   *All* of the following: below 5th centile for weight based on USA National Center for Health Statistics norms; no major organic disease which would affect capacity to gain weight; demonstration of weight gain in hospital; decreased rate of weight gain from birth to <5th centile; physical growth within norms for gestational age at birth; birth weight ≥ 1.5 kg.

SAMPLING FRAME/SIZE/DRAWBACKS   Fitted above FTT definition, aged 1–9 months at hospitalisation for NOFTT, absence of documented physical abuse and geographical proximity to researchers. Eighty-eight families fitted criteria; eight chose not to participate, 16 children moved/not traced/refused, five could not be located at follow-up; final sample size $n = 59$. Authors report attrition sample did not differ significantly from study group on demographic characteristics.

CONTROL/COMPARISON GROUP   No comparison groups with normal growth.

TYPE OF TREATMENT/THEORETICAL RATIONALE/WHO PROVIDES   Three types of intervention. Family-centred ($n = 22$) involved weekly home visits to the family group for about 12 months, working on enhancement of family coping skills, support to child's mother, especially organising the child's caretaking routines. Parent-centred ($n = 17$) involved supportive education (for about 12 months) focused on improving the quality of the mother's interactions, nutritional management and relationship with the child. Advocacy ($n = 20$) involved the child's mother being seen at home for an average of six visits over a two-month period, focused on providing emotional support and obtaining available economic and community resources; contact was maintained by a telephone for a further ten months.

FOCUS OF TREATMENT (CHILD? CARER?)   Family and/or mother.

LOCATION OF TREATMENT   Home based; Cleveland, Ohio, USA.

FOLLOW-UP PERIOD   At age 36 months (having been first assessed at average age 4.9 months, range 1–9 months).

OUTCOMES/EVALUATION (WHAT DEFINITION?)   Cognitive development (Stanford Binet IQ) of children ($n = 59$) at age 36 months. IQ declined between study intake and follow-up, regardless of type of early outreach intervention. One-way analysis of variance indicated no significant effect of type of intervention. Examiners assessing intellectual development were unaware of each child's treatment. Findings on specific intervention plans may have been blurred by non-specific variables included in intervention plans (e.g. outreach, continuity of care from hospital, emotional support to child's mother). Age range of 1–9 months at hospitalisation may encompass early-onset and late-onset FTT children, i.e. two distinct subtypes.

Hampton, D. (1996) 'Resolving the feeding difficulties associated with non-organic failure to thrive.' *Child: Care, Health and Development*, **22** (4), pp. 261–71.

TYPE OF STUDY   Reports on the evaluation of the Infant Support Project's work with children under 3 years referred for failure to thrive.

DEFINITION OF FTT   Weight falls below 3rd centile or deviates downwards from a previously established growth curve for three consecutive months.

SAMPLING FRAME/SIZE/DRAWBACKS   108 children referred to the Infant Support Project.

CONTROL/COMPARISON GROUP   None.

TYPE OF TREATMENT/THEORETICAL RATIONALE/WHO PROVIDES   The multi-disciplinary team comprised nursery nurses, health visitors and social workers, all employed by the voluntary organisation, The Children's Society, which operates the team. Referrals were from health or social care professionals; self-referrals were accepted. At referral children were given an FTT score depending on the number of FTT indicators (physical, psychological and social) evident at the time of referral. A single team member was then allocated as worker, although s/he consulted with colleagues in the course of the work. A number of assessment visits (including video recording of two meals) were undertaken, with a focus on forming a working alliance with parents. Parents also completed a food diary. A summary of findings at assessment was given to the parents; this included suggestions for work which then formed the basis of a working agreement. Work proceeded in the home, on the basis of planned ignoring and positive reinforcement.

FOCUS OF TREATMENT (CHILD? CARER?)   Child and parent(s).

LOCATION OF TREATMENT   Home; UK.

FOLLOW-UP PERIOD   There was an evaluation interview at the end of the course of work and again six months after work had finished.

OUTCOMES/EVALUATION (WHAT DEFINITION?)   For 108 children, 68% made progress regarded as satisfactory or better, i.e. weight gain and a reduction in their FTT score. Quarterly questionnaires were sent to parents using the project, asking about their satisfaction with the service. Of the 97 anonymous respondents to the question, 'How would you rate your contact with the project?', 90 reported it was good or excellent. Eighty-one of 94 respondents reported they had a written agreement for the work they were undertaking; of those with no agreement, eight were at the pre-agreement/planning stage.

Hanks, H. G. I., Hobbs, C. J., Seymour, D. and Stratton, P. (1988) 'Infants who fail to thrive: an intervention for poor feeding practices.' *Journal of Reproductive and Infant Psychology*, **6**, pp. 101–11.

TYPE OF STUDY   Exploration of brief intervention designed to enable mothers to feed children more adequately, assessed by effect on child's weight.

DEFINITION OF FTT   On or below 3rd centile on growth and developmental charts *or* 'substantial' falling of growth on centiles, *and* no physical ill health or handicap, *and* absence of severe developmental delay.

SAMPLING FRAME/SIZE/DRAWBACKS   Children aged under 4 years, on or below 3rd centile on growth and developmental charts (or 'substantial' falling of growth on centiles), no physical ill health or handicap, absence of severe developmental delay (using Denver Developmental Screening Inventory), not receiving other form of treatment, and parent/s prepared to take part in treatment plan. Twelve were put forward by health visitors who were concerned about these children's growth. Of the 12, 11 attended the clinic, ten were diagnosed by a paediatrician as FTT, two then ill, one mother refused and one withdrew, so sample *n* = 6, aged 11 to 18 months at entry.

CONTROL/COMPARISON GROUP   'The group of children provided their own control because previous weighing for every child had established a pattern of poor weight gain prior to entry into the study' (p. 103); authors suggest spontaneous improvement at this age (between 11 and 18 months) is unlikely 'once the pattern is well established'.

TYPE OF TREATMENT/THEORETICAL RATIONALE/WHO PROVIDES   Anthropometric measures and Denver Developmental Screening of the child, plus completion of questionnaires on general health, self-esteem and eating attitudes by the mother and an assessment session with a psychologist were followed by a mixture of psychodynamic, systemic and behavioural techniques. Sessions with the psychologist included discussions around dietary records, the children's behaviour, the importance of play, behaviour problems and methods of control, and the mothers' own experiences of childhood. The explicit focus was on feeding pattern. The mothers' acceptance that their child was failing to thrive was integral to treatment. Mothers and children attended for an average of five sessions across a 3–4 month period; children were weighed and measured by a health visitor at the start of each session. The context of the work was one of 'positive reframing', with the mothers recognising and taking credit for the improvements.

FOCUS OF TREATMENT (CHILD? CARER?)   The mothers (plus some fathers), with their children.

LOCATION OF TREATMENT   Child health clinic; Leeds, UK.

FOLLOW-UP PERIOD   Two months after the last session the children were weighed, measured and seen by a psychologist and paediatrician.

OUTCOMES/EVALUATION (WHAT DEFINITION?)   All gained weight rapidly during the intervention period; five out of the six also showed accelerated growth in height and head circumference; five were also significantly fatter. The GHQ, self-esteem and eating questionnaires did not identify a significant degree of psychological disturbance in the sample of mothers. This was very small scale, and only six of the 12 children identified were included in the study. There was no extended follow-up; the authors suggest 'booster sessions' would be needed to sustain improvement. However, the work took place in a very deprived area with modest resource implications, suggesting low cost community-based services such as this could be effective elsewhere.

Hobbs, C. and Hanks, H. G. I. (1996) 'A multidisciplinary approach for the treatment of children with failure to thrive.' *Child: Care, Health and Development*, **22** (4), pp. 273–84.

TYPE OF STUDY   Description of first 18 months of a multidisciplinary team's work with FTT children and their families.

DEFINITION OF FTT   Children who have failed to achieve expected growth as assessed by measurements of body size.

SAMPLING FRAME/SIZE/DRAWBACKS   All 67 children seen by the multidisciplinary team in the first 18 months of operation. All were referred by various professionals to the consultant community physician and then to the clinic team. Of the 67, 47 were seen on more than one occasion and so treated.

CONTROL/COMPARISON GROUP   None.

TYPE OF TREATMENT/THEORETICAL RATIONALE/WHO PROVIDES   The team comprised a health visitor, clinical psychologists, consultant community paediatrician, dietitian, community paediatrician and nursery nurse. They aimed to be supportive to one another and to the parents with whom they worked. Two professionals worked directly with each family whilst the other team members observed through a one-way screen. Normal team practice was that a full paediatric assessment was done plus clinical investigations if indicated by clinical need. Anthropometric measures were taken. There was liaison with primary care professionals. A feeding history was routinely taken and observation of a meal undertaken. Children's feeding behaviour was often observed in clinic consultations. The mean duration of the study families' attendance was 5.3 months, the mean number of appointments offered was 5.3 and appointments failed was 1.1.

FOCUS OF TREATMENT (CHILD? CARER?)   Child and parents.

LOCATION OF TREATMENT   Clinic plus home observation; Leeds, UK.

FOLLOW-UP PERIOD   Duration of attendance at the clinic (mean 5.3 months).

OUTCOMES/EVALUATION (WHAT DEFINITION?)   An overall improvement from a mean Z score of -2.17 to one of -1.87 (with a Z score of -2 roughly converting to the

3rd centile) at the end of treatment. Hobbs and Hanks conclude these changes are a significant improvement, as such an FTT group is known to be resistant to short- and long-term change.

Hutcheson, J.J., Black, M.M., Talley, M., Dubowitz, H., Howard. J.B., Starr, R.H. and Thompson, B.S. (1997) 'Risk status and home intervention among children with failure to thrive: follow-up at age 4.' *Journal of Pediatric Psychology*, **22** (5), pp. 651–68.

TYPE OF STUDY/LOCATION   Evaluation of home-based intervention; randomised clinical trial.

DEFINITION OF FTT   Weight for age below 5th percentile at 2 years or younger, having had birth weight appropriate for gestational age (minimum 36 weeks gestation).

SAMPLING FRAME/SIZE/DRAWBACKS   Children recruited from an urban paediatric primary care clinic; most being raised by single African-American mothers on public assistance. 130 children fitted criteria and were randomly allocated to clinic plus home intervention (64) or clinic only.

CONTROL/COMPARISON GROUP   66 children received clinic only intervention.

TYPE OF TREATMENT/THEORETICAL RATIONALE/WHO PROVIDES   All children received services in a multidisciplinary growth and nutrition clinic. A community-based agency provided weekly home visits for a year by a lay visitor supervised by a community health nurse. Visits focused on giving support, promoting parenting, child development, accessing resources and advocacy.

FOCUS OF TREATMENT (CHILD? CARER?)   Child and carer.

LOCATION OF TREATMENT   Clinic/home; Baltimore, USA.

FOLLOW-UP PERIOD   At age 4 years (at least one year after home intervention ceased).

OUTCOMES/EVALUATION (WHAT DEFINITION?)   Positive effects of the home intervention on motor development among all children, and on cognitive development and behaviour during play among children of mothers who reported low levels of negative affectivity toward their children.

McCann, B., Stein, A., Fairburn, C. G. and Dunger, D. B. (1994) 'Eating habits and attitudes of mothers of children with non-organic failure to thrive.' *Archives of Disease in Childhood*, **70**, pp. 234–6.

TYPE OF STUDY   Comparison of eating habits and attitudes concerning body shape and weight amongst mothers of FTT children (index group) with equivalent data on individually matched women (comparison group). Although not set up as an intervention study, all index group mothers received some treatment for their child's FTT and outcomes were reported.

DEFINITION OF FTT   Child's weight at referral was at or below the 3rd population centile, using Tanner and Whitehouse standards.

SAMPLING FRAME/SIZE/DRAWBACKS   Study was restricted to singleton children whose birth weight was above 2500 g with a gestation greater than 37 weeks. Twenty-six FTT children were identified from patient lists of two consultant paediatricians, having been referred by their GP in the past three years.

CONTROL/COMPARISON GROUP   Comparison group (although not for the purposes of evaluation of effectiveness of intervention).

TYPE OF TREATMENT/THEORETICAL RATIONALE/WHO PROVIDES   Mothers received advice on their child's diet, feeding and psychological management. They were encouraged to discuss feeding difficulties, how this made them feel and how their attitudes to food influenced management of their children's feeding difficulties.

FOCUS OF TREATMENT (CHILD? CARER?)   Mother.

LOCATION OF TREATMENT   Outpatient treatment; Oxfordshire, UK.

FOLLOW-UP PERIOD   Until discharge from outpatient clinic (length of treatment not given).

OUTCOMES/EVALUATION (WHAT DEFINITION?)   All children put on weight; at discharge their mean centile was 5th (range 3rd–25th centile). Mean weight deficit for height was 11.2%, a significant improvement compared with referral measures ($t = 4.35$, $p<0.001$). The five children who had grossly inadequate energy intake, as revealed by weekly recordings, responded best to treatment.

Powell, P. and Reid, P. (1994) 'A multidisciplinary assessment and treatment service for pre-school children with severe feeding problems.' *ACPP Review and Newsletter*, **16** (1), pp. 13–17.

TYPE OF STUDY/LOCATION   Clinical outcome for children under 30 months referred for FTT.

DEFINITION OF FTT   Failure to gain weight, or loss of weight.

SAMPLING FRAME/SIZE/DRAWBACKS   20 children referred specifically for failure to thrive to a feeding clinic team by paediatricians.

CONTROL/COMPARISON GROUP   Comparison of each child's weight at referral with weight at discharge.

TYPE OF TREATMENT/THEORETICAL RATIONALE/WHO PROVIDES   The multidisciplinary team comprised a dietitian, paediatrician, play specialist, psychologist, health visitor, social worker and speech/language therapist. An initial home visit for assessment by two team members was followed by parents completing a five-day food diary and having a meal at home video-recorded. At outpatients, children's height and weight was measured; for some there was also a clinical assessment through play. A feeding management programme was then negotiated with the parents, implemented with support provided by team members undertaking home visits and through telephone contact. Parents and children could attend a family support group, where staff worked with parents on child management strategies. Parents with very poor childhood experiences also had social work input; some received specialist help for personal difficulties. Average length of treatment for study children was 0.7 years.

FOCUS OF TREATMENT (CHILD? CARER?)   Child and parents.

LOCATION OF TREATMENT   Home and clinic; Clwyd, Wales.

FOLLOW-UP PERIOD   Treatment ceased after three months of satisfactory and consistent weight gain.

OUTCOMES/EVALUATION (WHAT DEFINITION?)   Each child's weight at referral and discharge was converted to standardised scores and a paired test conducted; the results were highly significant ($t = 14.13$, d.f. = 19, $p < 0.001$).

Sturm, L. and Drotar, D. (1989) 'Prediction of weight for height following intervention in three-year-old children with early histories of nonorganic faiurc to thrive.' *Child Abuse and Neglect*, **13** (1), pp. 19–28.

TYPE OF STUDY/LOCATION   Controlled study of efficacy of early intervention on the weight for height of NOFTT children; children randomly assigned to one of three interventions.

DEFINITION OF FTT   *All* of the following: below 5th centile for weight based on USA National Center for Health Statistics norms; no major organic disease which would affect capacity to gain weight; demonstration of weight gain in hospital; decreased rate of weight gain from birth to <5th centile; physical growth within norms for gestational age at birth; birth weight ≥1.5 kg.

SAMPLING FRAME/SIZE/DRAWBACKS   Fitted above FTT definition, aged 1–9 months at hospitalisation for NOFTT, absence of documented physical abuse and geographical proximity to researchers. Eighty-eight families fitted criteria; eight chose not to participate, 16 children moved/not traced/refused, five could not be located at follow-up; final sample size $n = 59$. Authors report attrition sample did not differ significantly from study group on demographic characteristics.

CONTROL/COMPARISON GROUP   No comparison groups with normal growth.

TYPE OF TREATMENT/THEORETICAL RATIONALE/WHO PROVIDES   Three types of intervention. Family-centred ($n = 22$) involved weekly home visits to the family group for about 12 months, working on enhancement of family coping skills, support to child's mother, especially organising the child's caretaking routines. Parent-centred ($n = 17$) involved supportive education (for about 12 months), focused on improving the quality of the mother's interactions, nutritional manage-ment and relationship with the child. Advocacy ($n = 20$) involved the child's mother being seen at home for an average of six visits over a two-month period, focused on providing emotional support and obtaining available economic and community resources; contact was maintained by a telephone for a further ten months.

FOCUS OF TREATMENT (CHILD? CARER?)   Family and/or mother.

LOCATION OF TREATMENT   Home based; Cleveland, Ohio, USA.

FOLLOW-UP PERIOD   At age 36 months (having been first assessed at average age 4.9 months, range 1–9 months).

OUTCOMES/EVALUATION (WHAT DEFINITION?)   The majority of children attained normal weight for height at outcome, although nearly one third demon-strated at least mild wasting. Type of outreach intervention did not affect weight for height at outcome. Shorter duration of FTT prior to diagnosis and greater initial rate of weight gain following hospitalisation predicted weight for height at 36 months. Findings on specific intervention plans may have been blurred by non-specific variables included in intervention plans (e.g. outreach, continuity of care from hospital, emotional support to child's mother). Age range of 1–9 months at hospitalisation may encompass early-onset and late-onset FTT children, i.e. two distinct subtypes.

Sullivan, B. (1991) 'Growth-enhancing interventions for nonorganic failure to thrive.' *Journal of Pediatric Nursing*, **6** (4), pp. 236–42.

TYPE OF STUDY   Effectiveness of two interventions compared.

DEFINITION OF FTT   Not known.

SAMPLING FRAME/SIZE/DRAWBACKS   Children aged 1–3 years who were FTT; the interaction behaviour of ten mother–child dyads.

CONTROL/COMPARISON GROUP   Comparison (see below)

TYPE OF TREATMENT/THEORETICAL RATIONALE/WHO PROVIDES   Some mothers received calorie management input, which focused on the children's nutritional intake. Others received 'socioemotional growth fostering interventions', which focused on healthy mother–child interaction behaviours.

FOCUS OF TREATMENT (CHILD? CARER?)   Mothers.

LOCATION OF TREATMENT   Not known whether home or clinic; USA.

FOLLOW-UP PERIOD   Not known.

OUTCOMES/EVALUATION (WHAT DEFINITION?)   A focus on nutritional intake seemed to enhance current mother–child conflicts. Children whose mothers received socioemotional growth fostering intervention showed greater weight gain and their mothers showed greater growth-enhancing behaviours.

Turner, K. M. T., Sanders, M. R. and Wall, C. R. (1994) 'Behavioral parent training versus dietary education in the treatment of children with persistent feeding difficulties.' *Behaviour Change*, **11** (4), pp. 242–58.

TYPE OF STUDY Controlled treatment outcome study to compare the effects of behavioural parent training (BPT) and standard dietary education (SDE) on the mealtime interaction, feeding behaviour, nutritional status and adjustment of children with feeding disorders. Children randomly assigned to treatments.

DEFINITION OF FTT Children aged 18 months to 5 years with persistent feeding difficulties.

SAMPLING FRAME/SIZE/DRAWBACKS 20 children and their families.

CONTROL/COMPARISON GROUP Comparison.

TYPE OF TREATMENT/THEORETICAL RATIONALE/WHO PROVIDES Initial screening included medical assessment, behavioural observation, mealtime interaction, nutritional intake analysis and self-report measures of parent and child adjustment.

FOCUS OF TREATMENT (CHILD? CARER?) Parents and (for BPT) children.

LOCATION OF TREATMENT Clinic; Australia.

FOLLOW-UP PERIOD Three to four months.

OUTCOMES/EVALUATION (WHAT DEFINITION?) Children in both treatment groups showed improvement on child behaviour measures at home and in mealtime observations in clinic. Children in both groups also showed an increase in the variety of foods sampled by follow-up. Mothers who received BPT showed more positive mother–child interaction during mealtimes. Treatment effects were maintained at follow-up.

Wright, C.M., Callum, J., Birks, E. and Jarvis, S. (1998) 'Effect of community based management in failure to thrive: randomised control trial.' *British Medical Journal*, **317**, pp. 571–4.

TYPE OF STUDY Randomised controlled trial to evaluate the effectiveness of a health visitor led intervention for FTT children under 2 years old.

DEFINITION OF FTT Screening programme required minimum of two weights: a baseline weight at 6–8 week check and a later weight submitted by health visitor, usually when infant was between 9 and 18 months old. If second weight standard deviation score (SDS2) showed a fall from baseline weight at 6 weeks (SDS1), after adjustment for regression to the mean using the Thrive Index measure (defined as [SDS2 − SDS1] × 0.65) then child was identified as FTT. The screening threshold used was a fall of 1.26 standard deviations, equivalent to a centile shift from the 50th to between the 10th and 3rd centile, which identifies the 5% of children with slowest gain.

SAMPLING FRAME/SIZE/DRAWBACKS   All children resident in Newcastle and born after October 1990 eligible for inclusion; no exclusions except for the second twin when a pair of twins was screened in. In all 229 FTT children were identified (a screening rate of 3% instead of the 5% expected, due to non-compliance with the screening programme by some health visitors). Twenty of the 38 primary care teams were randomly allocated to take part in intervention, giving 120 cases of FTT in intervention practices. Of these, 23 had no additional input as they recovered before identification, so there were 97 eligible children of whom 95 received standardised health visitor assessment at mean age of 15.6 (range 7–35) months.

CONTROL/COMPARISON GROUP   Control group of 109 FTT children whose health visitors received no additional training or support.

TYPE OF TREATMENT/THEORETICAL RATIONALE/WHO PROVIDES   Multidisciplinary group (liaison health visitor, research paediatrician and paediatric dietitian) provided introductory training to health visitors in intervention practices and then twice yearly sessions. Health visitors then conducted standardised assessments on identified FTT children, looked for dietary problems and provided advice. Dietitian input was offered to families and a medical examination by project paediatrician offered unless there was active hospital involvement. If FTT persisted, health visitors joined team meetings to discuss future management. In 16 children a referral was made for social work assessment; five others already had social worker involvement.

FOCUS OF TREATMENT (CHILD? CARER?)   Child and carer.

LOCATION OF TREATMENT   Home based by health visitor (who had access to multidisciplinary FTT team for consultation); Newcastle, UK.

FOLLOW-UP PERIOD   Follow-up at over age 3 years (mean age 45.2 months), when 57% of intervention group and 61% of controls seen.

OUTCOMES/EVALUATION (WHAT DEFINITION?)   Of those children seen at follow-up, intervention group children were significantly heavier and taller and were reported to have better appetites than children in control group, although both groups were equally satisfied with service. When children last weighed, 91 (76%) of intervention group had recovered from FTT compared with 60 (55%) control group ($p < 0.001$).

REFERENCES

American Psychiatric Association (1994) *Diagnostic and Statistical Manual of Mental Disorders*. New York: American Psychiatric Association.

Archer, L. and Szatmari, P. (1990) 'Assessment and treatment of food aversion in a four year old boy: a multidimensional approach.' *Canadian Journal of Psychiatry*, **35** (August), pp. 501–5.

Audit Commission (1994) *Seen but not Heard: Co-ordinating Community Child Health and Social Services for Children in Need*, Executive Summary. London: HMSO.

Barker, D. J. P. (1991) *The Childhood Environment and Adult Disease*. Chichester: Wiley.

Barnard, K. (1978) *Cognitive Growth Fostering Subscale of the Nursing Child Assessment Teaching Scale (NCAST)*. Seattle, USA: University of Washington.

Barnard, K. E. and Eyres, S. J. (1979) 'Child health assessment part 2: The first year of life.' US Department of Health, Education and Welfare, Public Health Service, HRA, Bureau of Health Manpower.

Batchelor, J. A. (1996) 'Has recognition of failure to thrive changed?' *Child: Care, Health and Development*, **22** (4), pp. 235–40.

Batchelor, J. and Kerslake, A. (1990) *Failure to Find Failure to Thrive: The Case for Improving Screening, Prevention and Treatment in Primary Care*. London: Whiting and Birch.

Benoit, D. (1993) 'Phenomenology and treatment of failure to thrive.' *Child and Adolescent Psychiatric Clinics of North America*, **2** (1), pp. 61–73.

Bithoney, W. G., McJunkin, J., Michalek, J., Egan, H., Snyder, J. and Munier, A. (1989) 'Prospective evaluation of weight gain in both non-organic and organic failure to thrive children: an outpatient trial of a multi-disciplinary team intervention strategy.' *Journal of Developmental and Behavioral Pediatrics*, **10** (1), pp. 27–31.

Bithoney, W. G., McJunkin, J., Michalek, J., Snyder, J., Egan, H. and Epstein, D. (1991) 'The effects of a multidisciplinary team approach on weight gain in nonorganic failure-to-thrive children.' *Journal of Developmental and Behavioral Pediatrics*, **12** (4), pp. 254–8.

Bithoney, W. G., Vansciver, M. M., Foster, S., Corso, S. and Tentindo, C. (1995) 'Parental stress and growth outcome in growth-deficient children.' *Pediatrics*, **96** (4), Pt 1, pp. 707–11.

Black, M. M., Dubowitz, H., Hutcheson, J., Berenson-Howard, J. and Starr, R. H. (1995) 'A randomized clinical trial of home intervention for children with failure to thrive.' *Pediatrics*, **95** (6), pp. 807–14.

Blissett, J. (1997) 'A feeding management programme.' Failure to Thrive Conference Proceedings, Cow and Gate National Conferences 1997.

Boddy, J. (1997) 'Maternal problem solving and the development of children who fail to thrive.' Failure to Thrive Conference Proceedings, Cow and Gate National Conferences 1997.

Boddy, J. M. and Skuse, D. H. (1994) 'Annotation: the process of parenting in failure to thrive.' *Journal of Child Psychology and Psychiatry*, **35** (3), pp. 401–24.

Bradley, R. H. (1993) 'Children's home environments, health, behavior and intervention efforts – a review using the HOME inventory as a marker measure.' *Genetic, Social and General Psychology Monographs*, **119** (4), pp. 439–90.

Budd, J. (1990) 'Falling short of the target.' *Community Care*, 15 November, pp. 21–2.

Caldwell, B. and Bradley, R. (1984) 'Home observation for the measurement of the environment.' Unpublished manuscript. Littlerock, USA:, University of Arkensas at Littlerock.

Casey, P. H., Kelleher, K. J., Bradley, R. H., Kellogg, K. W., Kirby, R. S. and Whiteside, L. (1994) 'A multifaceted intervention for infants with failure to thrive: a prospective study.' *Archives of Pediatric and Adolescent Medicine*, **148** (10), pp. 1071–7.

Cole, T. J. (1995) 'Conditional reference charts to assess weight gain in British infants.' *Archives of Disease in Childhood*, **73**, pp. 8–16.

Cole, T. J. (1997) '3-in-1 weight-monitoring chart.' *The Lancet*, **349**, pp. 102–3.

Corbett, S. S., Drewett, R. F. and Wright, C. M. (1996) 'Does a fall down a centile chart matter? The growth and developmental sequelae of mild failure to thrive.' *Acta Paediatrica*, **85** (11), pp. 1278–83.

Department of Health (1991) *Working Together Under the Children Act 1989.* London: HMSO.

Department of Health (1995) *Child Protection: Messages from Research.* London: HMSO.

Department of Health (1996) *Child Health in the Community: A Guide to Good Practice.* London: NHS Executive.

Douglas, J. (1991) 'Chronic and severe eating problems in young children.' *Health Visitor,* **64** (10), pp. 334–6.

Douglas, J. E. and Bryon, M. (1996) 'Interview data on severe behavioural eating difficulties in young children.' *Archives of Disease in Childhood,* **75** (4), pp. 304–8.

Drotar, D. (1988) 'Failure to thrive.' In D.K. Routh (ed.) *Handbook of Pediatric Psychology,* pp. 71–107. New York: Guilford Press.

Drotar, D. (1990) 'Sampling issues in research with nonorganic failure-to-thrive children.' *Journal of Pediatric Psychology,* **15** (2), pp. 255–72.

Drotar, D. (1991) 'The family context of nonorganic failure to thrive.' *American Journal of Orthopsychiatry,* **61** (1), pp. 23–34.

Drotar, D. (1994) 'Psychological research with pediatric conditions – if we specialize can we generalize?' *Journal of Pediatric Psychology,* **19** (4), pp. 403–14.

Drotar, D. and Sturm, L. (1988) 'Prediction of intellectual development in young children with early histories of non-organic failure to thrive.' *Journal of Pediatric Psychology,* **13** (2), pp. 281–96.

Drotar, D., Eckerle, D., Satola, J., Pallotta, J. and Wyatt, B. (1990) 'Maternal interactional behavior with nonorganic failure to thrive infants: a case comparison study.' *Child Abuse and Neglect,* **14**, pp. 41–51.

Edwards, A. G. K., Halse, P. C., Parkin, J. M. and Waterston, A. J. R. (1990) 'Recognising failure to thrive in early childhood.' *Archives of Disease in Childhood,* **65**, pp. 1263–5.

Edwards, A., Halse, P. and Waterston, T. (1994) 'Does poor weight gain identify children in need?' *Child Abuse Review,* **3**, pp. 107–19.

Frank, D. A. and Zeisel, S. H. (1988) 'Failure to thrive.' *Pediatric Clinics of North America,* **35** (6), pp. 1187–206.

Freeman, J. V., Cole, T. J., Chinn, S., Jones, P. R. M., White, E. M. and Preece, M. A. (1995) 'Cross sectional stature and weight reference curves for the UK, 1990.' *Archives of Disease in Childhood,* **73**, pp. 17–24.

Fryer, G. E. (1988) 'The efficacy of hospitalization of non-organic failure to thrive children: a meta-analysis.' *Child Abuse and Neglect,* **12**, pp. 375–81.

Goodman, R. (1994) 'Brain development.' In M. Rutter and D.F. Hay (eds) *Development through Life: A Handbook for Clinicians,* pp. 49–78. Oxford: Blackwell Scientific Publications.

Hakim-Larson, J., Voelker, S., Thomas, C. and Reinstein, L. (1997) 'Feeding and eating disorders.' In C.A. Essau and F. Petermann (eds) *Developmental*

Psychopathology: Epidemiology, Diagnostics and Treatment. The Netherlands: Harwood Academic Publishers.

Hampton, D. (1996) 'Resolving the feeding difficulties associated with non-organic failure to thrive.' *Child: Care, Health and Development*, **22** (4), pp. 261–71.

Hanks, H. and Hobbs, C. (1993) 'Failure to thrive – a model for treatment.' *Balliere's Clinical Paediatrics*, **1** (1), pp. 101–19.

Hanks, H. G. I., Hobbs, C. J., Seymour, D. and Stratton, P. (1988) 'Infants who fail to thrive: an intervention for poor feeding practices.' *Journal of Reproductive and Infant Psychology*, **6**, pp. 101–11.

Harris, G. and Booth, I. W. (1992) 'The nature and management of eating problems in pre-school children.' In P. Cooper and A. Stein (eds) *Feeding Problems and Eating Disorders in Children and Adolescents*. Philadelphia: Harwood Academic Publishers.

Harris, G. and Johnson, R. (1997) 'The development of taste and food preferences.' Failure to Thrive Conference Proceedings, Cow and Gate National Conferences 1997.

Heptinstall, E., Puckering, C., Skuse, D., Start, K., Zurszpiro, S. and Dowdney, L. (1987) 'Nutrition and mealtime behaviour in families of growth-retarded children.' *Human Nutrition: Applied Nutrition*, **41A**, pp. 390–402.

Hobbs, C. and Hanks, H. G. I. (1996) 'A multidisciplinary approach for the treatment of children with failure to thrive.' *Child: Care, Health and Development*, **22** (4), pp. 273–84.

Hobbs, C. J., Hanks, H. G. I. and Wynne, J. M. (1993) *Child Abuse and Neglect: A Clinician's Handbook*. Edinburgh: Churchill Livingstone.

Hutcheson, J. J., Black, M. M., Talley, M., Dubowitz, H., Howard, J. B., Starr, R. H. and Thompson, B. S. (1997) 'Risk status and home intervention among children with failure to thrive: follow-up at age 4.' *Journal of Pediatric Psychology*, **22** (5), pp. 651–68.

Iwaniec, D. (1996) *The Emotionally Abused and Neglected Child*. Chichester: Wiley.

Lindberg, L., Bohlin, G., Hagekull, B. and Palmerus, K. (1996) 'Interactions between mothers and infants showing food refusal.' *Infant Mental Health Journal*, **7** (4), pp. 334–47.

Lobo, M. L., Barnard, K. E. and Coombs, J. B. (1992) 'Failure to thrive: a parent–infant interaction perspective.' *Journal of Pediatric Nursing*, **7** (4), pp. 251–61.

Lucas, A., Cole, T. J. and Gandy, G. M. (1986) 'Birthweight centiles in preterm infants reappraised.' *Early Human Development*, **13**, pp. 313–22.

Mackner, L. M., Starr, R. H. and Black, M. M. (1997) 'The cumulative effect of neglect and failure to thrive on cognitive functioning.' *Child Abuse and Neglect*, **21** (7), pp. 691–700.

Marcovitch, H. (1994) 'Failure to thrive.' *British Medical Journal*, **308** (6920), pp. 35–8.

Mathisen, B., Skuse, D., Wolke, D. and Reilly, S. (1989) 'Oral-motor dysfunction and failure to thrive among inner-city infants.' *Developmental Medicine and Child Neurology*, **31**, pp. 293–302.

McCann, J. B., Stein, A., Fairburn, C. G. and Dunger, D. B. (1994) 'Eating habits and attitudes of mothers of children with non-organic failure to thrive.' *Archives of Disease in Childhood*, **70**, pp. 234-6.

Miguel, S. A. and Burton, S. D. (1990) 'Failure-to-thrive: a parent's viewpoint.' *Early Child Development and Care*, **61**, pp. 77–80.

Minty, B. and Patterson, G. (1994) 'The nature of child neglect.' *British Journal of Social Work*, **24**, pp. 733– 48.

Moores, J. (1997) 'Weaning and failure to thrive.' Failure to Thrive Conference Proceedings, Cow and Gate National Conferences 1997.

Neden, J. (1996) 'Deconstructing failure to thrive: A model for social work assessment of families with a child diagnosed as failing to thrive.' Unpublished M.A. dissertation. Newcastle: University of Northumberland in Newcastle upon Tyne.

Nelson, M., Margetts, B. M. and Black, A. E. (1993) 'Letters to the Editors: Checklist for the methods section of dietary investigations.' *British Journal of Nutrition*, **69**, pp. 935 40.

O'Hagan, K. (1993) *Emotional and Psychological Abuse of Children*. Buckingham: Open University Press.

Parton, N. (1996) 'Child protection, family support and social work: a critical appraisal of the Department of Health research studies in child protection.' *Child and Family Social Work*, **1** (1), pp. 3–11.

Polan, H. J., Leon, A., Kaplan, M. D., Kessler, D. B., Stern, D. N. and Ward, M. J. (1991) 'Disturbances of affect expression in failure to thrive.' *Journal American Academy of Child and Adolescent Psychiatry*, **30** (6), pp. 897–903.

Powell, P. and Reid, P. (1994) 'A multidisciplinary assessment and treatment service for pre-school children with severe feeding problems.' *ACPP Review and Newsletter*, **16** (1), pp. 13–17.

Puckering, C., Pickles, A., Skuse, D., Hepinstall, E., Dowdney, L. and Zurszpiro, S. (1995) 'Mother–child interaction and the cognitive and behavioral development of 4-year-old children with poor growth.' *Journal of Child Psychology and Psychiatry and Allied Disciplines*, **36** (4), pp. 573–95.

Ramsay, M. (1995) 'Feeding disorders and failure to thrive.' *Infant Psychiatry*, **4** (3), pp. 605–16.

Ramsay, M. and Gisel, E. G. (1996) 'Neonatal sucking and maternal feeding practices.' *Developmental Medicine and Child Neurology*, **38** (1), pp. 34–47.

Ramsay, M., Gisel, E. G. and Boutry, M. (1993) 'Non-organic failure to thrive: growth failure secondary to feeding skills disorder.' *Developmental Medicine and Child Neurology*, **35**, pp. 285–97.

Reif, S., Beler, B., Villa, Y. and Spirer, Z. (1995) 'Long-term follow-up and outcome of infants with non-organic failure to thrive.' *Israeli Journal of Medical Science*, **31** (8), pp. 483–89.

Reifsnider, E. (1995) 'The use of human ecology and epidemiology in nonorganic failure to thrive.' *Public Health Nursing*, **12** (4), pp. 262–8.

Reilly, S. (1997) 'Oral-motor dysfunction.' Failure to Thrive Conference Proceedings, Cow and Gate National Conferences 1997.

Reilly, S., Skuse, D., Mathisen, B. and Wolke, D. (1995) 'The objective rating of oral-motor functions during feeding.' *Dysphagia*, **10**, pp. 177–91.

Russell, G. F., Treasure, J. and Eisler, I. (1998) 'Mothers with anorexia nervosa who underfeed their children: their recognition and management.' *Psychological Medicine*, **28** (1), pp. 93–108.

Savage, S. A. H., Reilly, J. J. and Durnin, J. V. (1996) 'Weight and length of Glasgow infants compared with Tanner and Whitehouse standards and new British standards for growth.' *Proceedings of the Nutrition Society*, **55**, p. 81A.

Schmitt, B. D. and Mauro, R. D. (1989) 'Nonorganic failure to thrive: an outpatient process.' *Child Abuse and Neglect*, **13**, pp. 235–48.

Skuse, D. (1993) 'Identification and management of problem eaters.' *Archives of Disease in Childhood*, **69**, pp. 604–8.

Skuse, D., Reilly, S. and Wolke, D. (1992) 'Failure to thrive: clinical and developmental aspects.' In H. Remschmidt and M. Schmidt (eds) *Child and Youth Psychiatry: European Perspectives*, pp. 46–71. Gottingen: Hogrefe and Huber.

Skuse, D., Pickles, A., Wolke, D. and Reilly, S. (1994a) 'Postnatal growth and mental development: evidence for a sensitive period.' *Journal of Child Psychology and Psychiatry*, **35** (3), pp. 521–45.

Skuse, D., Reilly, S. and Wolke, D. (1994b) 'Psychosocial adversity and growth during infancy.' *European Journal of Clinical Nutrition*, **48** (Suppl. 1), pp. S113–S130.

Skuse, D. H., Gill, D., Wolke, D. and Lynch, M. A. (1995) 'Failure to thrive and the risk of child abuse: a prospective population survey.' *Journal of Medical Screening*, **2**, pp. 145–9.

Smart, J. L. (1991) 'Critical periods in brain development.' In G. R. Bock and J. Whelan (eds) *The Childhood Environment and Adult Disease*, pp. 109–28. London: Wiley.

Smith, M. M. and Lifshitz, F. (1994) 'Excess fruit juice consumption as a contributing factor in nonorganic failure to thrive.' *Pediatrics*, **93** (3), pp. 438–43.

Stein, A., Woolley, H., Cooper, S. D. and Fairburn, C. (1994) 'An observational study of mothers with eating disorders and their infants.' *Journal of Child Psychology and Psychiatry*, **35** (4), pp. 733–48.

Stein, A., Stein, J., Walters, E. A. and Fairburn, C. G. (1995) 'Eating habits and attitudes among mothers of children with feeding disorders.' *British Medical Journal*, **310**, p. 228.

Stevenson, O. (1995) 'Emotional abuse and neglect: a time for reappraisal.' *Child and Family Social Work*, **1** (1), pp. 13–18.

Stordy, B. J., Redfern, A. M. and Morgan, J. B. (1995) 'Healthy eating for infants – mothers' actions.' *Acta Paediatrica*, **84**, pp. 733–41.

Sturm, L. and Drotar, D. (1989) 'Prediction of weight for height following intervention in three-year-old children with early histories of nonorganic failure to thrive.' *Child Abuse and Neglect*, **13** (1), pp. 19–28.

Sullivan, B. (1991) 'Growth-enhancing interventions for nonorganic failure to thrive.' *Journal of Pediatric Nursing*, **6** (4), pp. 236–42.

Tanner, J. M. and Whitehouse, R. H. (1959) 'Standards for height and weight of British children from birth to maturity.' *Lancet*, **2**, pp. 1086–8.

Turner, K. M. T., Sanders, M. R. and Wall, C. R. (1994) 'Behavioral parent training versus dietary education in the treatment of children with persistent feeding difficulties.' *Behavior Change*, **11** (4), pp. 242–58.

Ward, M. J., Kessler, D. B. and Altman, S. C. (1993) 'Infant–mother attachment in children with failure to thrive.' *Infant Mental Health Journal*, **14** (3), pp. 208–20.

Weston, J. A. and Colloton, M. (1993) 'A legacy of violence in non-organic failure to thrive.' *Child Abuse and Neglect*, **17** (6), pp. 709–14.

Whitten, C. F., Pettit, M. G. and Fischhoff, J. (1969) 'Evidence that growth failure from maternal deprivation is secondary to undereating.' *Journal of American Medical Association*, **209**, pp. 1675–82.

Wilcox, W. D., Nieburg, P. and Miller, D. S. (1989) 'Failure to thrive: a continuing problem of definition.' *Clinical Pediatrics (Philadelphia)*, **28** (9), pp. 391–4.

Wilensky, D. S., Ginsberg, G., Altman, M., Tulchinsky, T. H., Yishay, F. B. and Auerbach, J. (1996) 'A community based study of failure to thrive in Israel.' *Archives of Disease in Childhood*, **75**, pp. 145–8.

Williams, A. (1994) 'Ensuring a healthy start: preventing failure to thrive in infants.' *Child Health*, **2** (2), pp. 68–72.

Wolke, D. (1994) 'Sleeping and feeding across the lifespan.' In M. Rutter and D. F. Hay (eds) *Development through Life: A Handbook for Clinicians*, pp. 517–57. Oxford: Blackwell Scientific Publications.

Wolke, D. (1996) 'Failure to thrive: the myth of maternal deprivation syndrome.' *The Signal: Newsletter of the World Association for Infant Mental Health*, **4** (3/4), pp. 1–6.

Wolke, D. and Skuse, D. (1992) 'The management of infant feeding problems.' In P. Cooper and A. Stein (eds) *Feeding Problems and Eating Disorders in Children and Adolescents: Monographs in Clinical Pediatrics*, **5**, pp. 27–59. Philadelphia: Harwood Academic Publishers.

World Health Organisation (1992) *The ICD-10 Classification of Mental and Behavioural Disorders: Clinical Descriptions and Diagnostic Guidelines*. Geneva: WHO.

Wright, C. M. (1995) 'A population approach to weight monitoring and failure to thrive.' In T. J. David (ed.) *Recent Advances in Paediatrics*, **13**, pp. 73–87. Edinburgh: Churchill Livingstone.

Wright, C. M. and Talbot, E. (1996) 'Screening for failure to thrive – what are we looking for?' *Child: Care, Health and Development*, **22** (4), pp. 223–34.

Wright, C., Matthews, J. N. S., Waterston, A. and Aynsley-Green, A. (1994a) 'What is a normal rate of weight gain in infancy?' *Acta Paediatrica*, **83**, pp. 351–6.

Wright, C., Waterston, A. and Aynsley-Green, A. (1994b) 'Effect of deprivation on weight gain in infancy.' *Acta Paediatrica*, **83**, pp. 357–9.

Wright, C., Avery, A., Epstein, M., Birks, E. and Croft, D. (1998a) 'New chart to evaluate weight faltering.' *Archives of Disease in Childhood*, **78**, pp. 40–3.

Wright, C. M., Callum, J., Birks, E. and Jarvis, S. (1998b) 'Effect of community based management in failure to thrive: randomised control trial.' *British Medical Journal*, **317**, pp. 571–4.

INDEX

abuse, child 20, 35–8
  emotional 35–6, 38, 57, 79
  evidence for and against FTT as
    36–8
  interventions 59, 67, 79, 89
  and professional beliefs 20, 35–6,
    57, 67, 83, 91
  use of term 18
abuse, maternal history of 53–4, 68
accidental FTT 38
adult health and illness 1
advocacy
  for families 58
  groups 63, 65
aetiology *see* causal factors
affluent families 22
age at onset 26–8, 93
American Psychiatric Association 5, 48
anaemia 40, 50
anorexic mothers 52–3
appetite regulation system 41
Archer, L. 53, 68, 77, 101 Appendix
Asian mothers 50
assessment 56, 59
  development of better models 94
  dietary 15, 86–7
  of family and social factors 87
  of feeding problems 67, 69, 70
  of feeding skills 87
  initial 84–5
  second stage 86–9

attachment behaviour 48, 49–50
Audit Commission 99

Barker, D. J. P. 1
Barnard, K. 40, 87
Batchelor, J. 19, 20, 22, 31, 83, 99
behavioural interventions 68, 69, 70–1
Benoit, D. 5, 35, 39, 79
biases in research samples 3 4, 15
Bithoney, W. G. *et al.* 34–5, 58, 77, 80,
  101–3 Appendix
Black, M. M. *et al.* 74, 103 Appendix
Blissett, J. 50
Boddy, J. M. 15, 20, 47, 49–50, 92,
  94–5, 97
Booth, I. W. 40, 43, 68–9
Bradley, R. 39, 87
brain development abnormalities 23,
  27
breast-feeding 22, 41, 44–5
British Standards growth charts 6
Bryon, M. 35, 40, 46, 52
Buckler, J.M.H. 5
Budd, J. 35, 36
Burton, S. D. 76

Caldwell, B. 39, 87
carers
  causal factors and 4, 39, 41–2,
    47–54
  effects on 28–32, 53

group work with 76
in institutions 2
mental health of 53–4
views of services 98
see also mothers; parents
case studies 68
  1: Amina 6, 7
  2: Kieron 23, 24–5, 31
  3: Saul 29, 30–1
  4: child and family factors 37, 41–2
  5: parents' experiences of interventions 77, 78
Casey, P. H. *et al.* 65–6, 104 Appendix
catch-up growth 27, 59, 73
causal factors 3, 15, 34–55, 93
  and abuse or neglect 35–9
  current thinking 3–5
  infant/child factors 4, 39, 41–6, 92, 93
  insufficient calories established as cause 3
  and interactional perspective 4, 28, 39–40
  mother/carer factors 4, 39, 41–2, 47–54
  multifactorial aetiology 4–5, 17, 94–5
  organic *vs* non-organic 34–5
centile charts *see* charting of growth; growth centile charts
charting of growth 5–7, 14, 19, 20, 83, 91–2
child, effects of FTT on 23–6
child abuse *see* abuse, child
child health computers 83
child/infant causal factors 4, 39, 41–6, 92, 93
child protection issues 15, 36, 38, 89
Children Act 1989 79, 82, 97, 99
Children's Society, The 80–1
  Feeding Matters programme 17, 98–9
  Infant Support Project 61–2
children's views of services 98
classification 5

clinical samples and bias 3–4, 15, 37, 91
clinic-based *vs* home-based treatment 74–5, 92
cognitive development
  effects on 23, 26, 27, 38, 39
  outcomes from intervention studies 63, 65–6, 74, 75
Cole, T. J. 14
Colloton, M. 53–4, 87
communication between researchers and practitioners 91–3, 100
communication of needs in infants 43, 45, 46, 68
Community Growth and Nutrition Service (Newcastle) 98–9
compensatory parenting 46, 48–9, 94
conclusions and recommendations 91–100
  developing best practice 94–9
  development of better models of assessment and intervention 94
  dialogue between researchers and practitioners 91–3
  effective services 95–6
  efficiency of services 97–8
  examples of good practice 98–9
  future developments 99
  key issues 91–4
  recommendations 100
  understanding importance of FTT 93
Corbett, S. S. *et al.* 23
cost of multidisciplinary teams 97

definitions 5–14, 21, 82–3, 91–2
deliberate FTT 38
Department of Health 6, 15, 36
depression in mothers 53
deprivation 2, 4, 20, 22, 26–7, 40, 58, 88
  see also emotional deprivation; maternal deprivation
developmental checks, timing of 100
developmental delay 23–6, 38

developmental status of infants 43
Diagnostic and Statistical Manual 5, 48
dietary assessments 15, 86–7
dietitians 80, 81
Douglas, J. 53
Douglas, J. E. 35, 40, 46, 52
Drotar, D. 14, 15, 37, 38, 39, 47, 54, 57, 58, 63–4, 65, 77, 92, 104–5 Appendix, 111–12 Appendix
Drotar, D. *et al.* 47

early onset FTT 26–8, 37, 53, 93
eating attitudes/habits of mothers 51–3, 61
'Eco-Epi' model 39–40
Edwards, A. *et al.* 6–7, 82
effects 23–32, 93
    on carers, family and professionals 28–32, 53, 80
    on child 23–6
    and neglect 39
emotional deprivation 3, 35–6, 57
endocrine function 3
environmental factors 22, 39, 40, 58
epidemiological studies 4, 21–3, 91
ethnic group differences 21, 50, 83
Eyres, S. J. 40

false positives 28
family, effects on 28–32
family causal factors 4, 39, 41–2, 47–54
family-centred interventions 63, 65, 79
family systems model 76
fat levels in diet 59–60, 85
Feeding Assessment Schedule 45
feeding difficulties/disorders 4, 16, 24–5, 29–31, 93
    classification 5
    and compensatory parenting 48–9
    and eating habits/attitudes of mothers 51, 52, 61
    feeding skills disorders 4, 43–4, 87

improving identification 95
interactional model 40
and mental health of carers 53
relationship to abuse/neglect 36–7
relationship to FTT 66–7
studies of interventions 60–1, 67–71
feeding history 69, 87
feeding practices at weaning 50
feeding skills assessment 87
fluid intake 50
food diaries 59, 61, 62, 86
food refusal 50, 66–8
Frank, D. A. 34, 35, 59, 73
Freeman, J. V. *et al.* 14
fruit juice 50
Fryer, G. E. 73

gender-blindness in research 15
Gisel, E. G. 49
Goodman, R. 27
group work with caregivers/parents 61, 76, 88
growth centile charts 5–7, 14, 19, 20, 83, 91–2
growth hormone deficiency 35–6

Hakim-Larson, J. *et al.* 5
Hampton, D. 61–2, 76–7, 81, 106 Appendix
Hanks, H. G. I. 37, 59, 62, 77, 79, 80, 81, 108–9 Appendix
Hanks, H. G. I. *et al.* 36–7, 77, 107–8 Appendix
Harris, G. 17, 40, 43, 68–9
health visitors 31
    and interventions 63, 80–1
    and recognition of FTT 19, 22, 83
Heptinstall, E. *et al.* 45, 46
hierarchical approach to intervention 85
high calorie supplements 60
high chairs 50

history of understanding of FTT 2–3
Hobbs, C. 37, 59, 62, 77, 79, 80, 81,
    108–9 Appendix
Hobbs, C. J. *et al.* 59, 74
home-based interventions 81–2, 86
    vs clinic-based 74–5, 92
home observations 87
home-prepared weaning foods 50
HOME scales or inventories 39, 87
hospitalisation 35, 73–4
hospitalised samples 15, 47, 63–4, 65
Hutcheson, J. J. *et al.* 74, 109 Appendix

identification 19–20, 22–3
    improvement of 95
    strategy for identifying children with
        poor growth 82–4
infant/child causal factors 4, 39, 41–6, 92,
    93
infant developmental status 43
infant-focused interventions 79
infant growth coordinators 99, 100
institutional care of children 2
interactional perspective 4, 28, 39–40
'interactional synchrony' 49
interventions 1–2, 15–16, 56–72
    cognitive development outcomes
        from studies 63, 65–6, 74, 75
    context of FTT provision 97–8
    developing best practice 94–9
    development of better models 94
    early intervention 84–5
    effective services 82–9, 92, 95–6
    efficiency of services 97–8
    evaluation of services 98
    feeding disorders studies 66–71
    growth outcomes from single inter-
        vention studies 60–3
    growth outcomes from studies
        comparing different interventions
        63–5
    health visitor led 63

how to treat 76–9
    model for effective intervention 82–9
    models 39–40, 73–90, 94, 97
    nutritional intervention 59–60, 64–5
    overviews and summaries of research
        and clinical practice 58–60
    parents' experiences/views 76–9, 82,
        84, 85, 98
    points for intervention 27, 52, 60, 64,
        71, 84, 85, 88
    preliminary notes on studies 57–8
    research studies of programmes
        101–14 Appendix
    second stage 86–9
    strategy for identifying children with
        poor growth 82–4
    where to treat 73–5
    who should treat 79–82
invasive medical techniques 35, 86–7
IQ
    of child 23, 66
    of mother 49
Iwaniec, D. 17, 79

Johnson, R. 69

Kerslake, A. 19, 20, 22, 31, 83

late-onset FTT 26–7, 53
Lifshitz, F. 50
Lindberg, L. *et al.* 43
Lobo, M. L. *et al.* 40, 87
Lucas, A. *et al.* 14

McCann, J. B. *et al.* 51, 60–1, 77, 87,
    109–10 Appendix
Mackner, L. M. *et al.* 39
malnutrition 2, 3, 34
maltreatment/'harm' distinction 38
Marcovitch, H. 35, 38, 79
maternal deprivation 3, 15, 47, 49, 92
Mathisen, B. *et al.* 45–6

Mauro, R. D. 38
mealtimes
as stressful occasions 29
video recording of 59, 61, 62, 84–5, 87
medical model 18, 75, 96
mental health of carers 53–4
methodological problems in research 14–16
methodology used in review 16–17
Miguel, S. A. 76
Minty, B. 38
models of intervention 39–40, 73–90, 94, 97
Moores, J. 59–60
mother–child relationships 3, 4, 79
mother-focused interventions 79
mother–infant attachments 49–50
mother–infant/child interactions 15, 26, 36–7, 43, 44, 47–8, 49, 51, 64–5, 68, 69
mothers
Asian 50
causal factors and 47–54
eating attitudes/habits of 51–3, 61
history of abuse in 53–4, 68
IQ 49
problem-solving strategies 49–50, 92
multidisciplinary teams 59, 61–2, 69, 86
case for 79–82
community-based 96
cost 97
and developing best practice 94, 95–6, 97, 100
hospital-based 96
structure and composition 80–2

Neden, J. 76
neglect 1, 18, 20, 32, 35–9
effects of FTT and 39

evidence for and against FTT as 36–8
interventions 59, 67, 79, 89
neglectful FTT 38
'neglect of' 38
parental culpability in 37–8
and professional beliefs 20, 35–6, 57, 67, 83, 91
Nelson, M. et al. 15
non-organic FTT
causal factors 3, 4–5, 34–5, 36, 38, 39, 44, 49, 53–4, 57–8, 92
non-organic/organic distinction 3, 4–5, 34–5, 57–8
non-verbal communication in infants 43
normal growth variations 6
nursery nurses 81
Nursing Child Assessment Feeding and Teaching Scales 87
nutritional advice 59–60, 85
nutritional deficiencies 40, 50
nutritional intervention 59–60, 64–5, 73, 96
nutritionists 80

observation of feeding 59, 87
O'Hagan, K. 37
oral hypersensitivity 45–6
oral-motor dysfunction 4, 41, 44–6, 48, 69, 87, 93
organic FTT 3, 20
organic/non-organic distinction 3, 4–5, 34–5, 57–8
overweight mothers 53

paediatricians 31, 80, 81, 96
paediatric nurses 64, 80
parent-centred interventions 63, 65
parent–child interactions 47–50, 87
parent-held records 83, 84
parenting

as causal factor 26–7, 47–50
compensatory 46, 48–9, 94
parents
    culpability in neglect 37–8
    effects on 28–32
    experiences/views of interventions
        76–9, 82, 84, 85, 98
    group work with 61, 76, 88
    see also carers; mothers
parent training 70–1
Parkin Project (Newcastle) 14, 63, 76
Parton, N. 15
Patterson, G. 38
points for intervention 27, 52, 60, 64, 71,
    84, 85, 88
Polan, H. J. *et al.* 43
'positive reframing' of behaviour 77
postnatal depression 53
poverty 2, 4, 20, 22, 26–7, 40, 58, 88
Powell, P. 38, 61, 77, 81, 110–11
    Appendix
predisposition to FTT 35–6, 41
preterm infants 65–6, 92
prevalence 21–3
primary health care staff 19, 22, 84
professionals
    communication between researchers
        and practitioners 91–3, 100
    differences of view between 17–18
    effects on 31, 80
    and improving identification 95
    preconceptions and recognition of
        FTT 19–20, 22–3, 35–6, 57, 67, 83,
        91
    stress in 80
    training 83–4, 94, 96, 97, 100
    see also health visitors;
        multidisciplinary teams; social
        workers
psychiatrists 80
psychologists 80, 81–2
psychology, developments in 47, 97

psychosocial assessment 67
psychosocial dimension in treatment 58,
    59, 60, 64, 69, 73, 81–2, 96
psychosocial dwarfism 57
Puckering, C. *et al.* 23, 26

Ramsay, M. 17, 40, 43, 46, 48–9, 54, 70,
    80, 97
Ramsay, M. *et al.* 44, 77, 87
recommendations 100
Reid, P. 38, 61, 77, 81, 110–11 Appendix
Reif, S. *et al.* 23
Reifsnider, E. 39–40
Reilly, S. 45, 49
Reilly, S. *et al.* 87
research studies of intervention
    programmes 101–14 Appendix
responsiveness level in infants 43
Russell, G. F. *et al.* 52–3

Savage, S. A. H. *et al.* 6
Schedule for Oral Motor Assessment 87
Schmitt, B. D. 38
sensitive/critical periods 26–7
services *see* interventions
Skuse, D. H. 15, 20, 35–6, 40, 41, 43–4,
    47, 49, 54, 69, 80, 92, 94–5, 97
Skuse, D. H. *et al.* 3, 4, 14, 20, 21, 23, 26,
    35, 37, 43, 44, 48, 49, 50, 53, 57, 87,
    92
Smart, J. L. 27
Smith, M. M. 50
social reinforcement techniques 69
social services departments 97
social workers 36, 38, 57, 80, 81
socioemotional growth fostering inter-
    ventions 64–5
speech therapists 80, 81
Stein, A. *et al.* 51, 52, 87
Stevenson, O. 37–8
stigmatisation and parents 67
stimulation, lack of 2

Stordy, B. J. *et al.* 50
Sturm, L. 63–4, 65, 104–5 Appendix, 111–12 Appendix
sucking ability in infants 49
sugar levels in diet 59–60
Sullivan, B. 64–5, 112 Appendix
supplements, use of 60
Szatmari, P. 53, 68, 77, 101 Appendix

Talbot, E. 20, 22, 34, 35, 38, 76, 83, 85, 97
Tanner, J. M. 5–6, 7
temperament 4, 40, 49
Thrive Index 7, 14, 19, 22, 38
timing of FTT 26–8, 93
training of professionals 83–4, 94, 96, 97, 100
treatments *see* interventions
Turner, K. M. T. *et al.* 70, 113 Appendix
two-dimensional treatment model 59, 65, 73
two-tier treatment model 58

video recording of mealtimes 59, 61, 62, 84–5, 87

views of children/parents/carers 76–9, 82, 84, 85, 98
vomiting 46, 68

Ward, M. J. *et al.* 47–8
weaning, feeding practices at 50
weight charts 5–7, 14, 19, 20, 83, 91–2
Weston, J. A. 53–4, 87
Whitehouse, R. H. 5, 6, 7
Whitten, C. F. *et al.* 3
Wilcox, W. D. *et al.* 14
Wilensky, D. S. *et al.* 4, 15, 21, 23, 44–5
Williams, A. 39, 40, 77
Wolke, D. 2, 4, 14, 15, 21, 23, 26, 35, 37, 38, 41, 43, 44, 49, 50, 53, 57, 69, 80
Working Together under the Children Act 1989 36
World Health Organization 5
Wright, C. M. 6–7, 14, 19, 20, 22, 23, 27, 34, 35, 38, 40, 76, 83, 85
Wright, C. M. *et al.* 7, 14, 22, 63, 74, 81, 83, 97, 113–14 Appendix

Zeisel, S. H. 34, 35, 59, 73

The Children's Society
A positive force for change

The Children's Society is one of Britain's leading charities for children and young people. Founded in 1881 as a Christian organisation, The Children's Society reaches out unconditionally to children and young people regardless of race, culture or creed.

Over 90 projects throughout England and Wales
We work with over 30,000 children of all ages, focusing on those whose circumstances have made them particularly vulnerable. We aim to help to stop the spiral into isolation, anger and lost hope faced by so many young people.

We constantly look for effective, new ways of making a real difference
We measure local impact and demonstrate through successful practice that major issues can be tackled and better resolved. The Children's Society has an established track record of taking effective action: both in changing public perceptions about difficult issues such as child prostitution, and in influencing national policy and practice to give young people a better chance at life.

The Children's Society is committed to overcoming injustice wherever we find it
We are currently working towards national solutions to social isolation, lack of education and the long-term problems they cause, through focused work in several areas:

- helping parents whose babies and toddlers have inexplicably stopped eating, endangering their development;
- involving children in the regeneration of poorer communities;
- preventing exclusions from primary and secondary schools;
- providing a safety net for young people who run away from home and care;
- seeking viable alternatives to the damaging effects of prison for young offenders.

The Children's Society will continue to raise public awareness of difficult issues to promote a fairer society for the most vulnerable children in England and Wales. For further information about the work of The Children's Society or to obtain a publications catalogue, please contact:

The Children's Society, Publishing Department, Edward Rudolf House, Margery Street, London WC1X 0JL. Tel. 0171 841 4400. Fax 0171 841 4500.

Website address: http://www.the-childrens-society.org.uk

The Children's Society is a registered charity: Charity Registration No. 221124.